Consort, Full, and Verse Anthems

RECENT RESEARCHES IN MUSIC

A-R Editions publishes seven series of critical editions, spanning the history of Western music, American music, and oral traditions.

RECENT RESEARCHES IN THE MUSIC OF THE MIDDLE AGES AND EARLY RENAISSANCE
   Charles M. Atkinson, general editor

RECENT RESEARCHES IN THE MUSIC OF THE RENAISSANCE
   James Haar, general editor

RECENT RESEARCHES IN THE MUSIC OF THE BAROQUE ERA
   Christoph Wolff, general editor

RECENT RESEARCHES IN THE MUSIC OF THE CLASSICAL ERA
   Eugene K. Wolf, general editor

RECENT RESEARCHES IN THE MUSIC OF THE NINETEENTH AND EARLY TWENTIETH CENTURIES
   Rufus Hallmark, general editor

RECENT RESEARCHES IN AMERICAN MUSIC
   John M. Graziano, general editor

RECENT RESEARCHES IN THE ORAL TRADITIONS OF MUSIC
   Philip V. Bohlman, general editor

Each edition in *Recent Researches* is devoted to works by a single composer or to a single genre. The content is chosen for its high quality and historical importance, and each edition includes a substantial introduction and critical report. The music is engraved according to the highest standards of production using the proprietary software MusE, owned by Music | Notes™, Inc.

For information on establishing a standing order to any of our series, or for editorial guidelines on submitting proposals, please contact:

A-R Editions, Inc.
801 Deming Way
Madison, Wisconsin 53717

800 736-0070 (U.S. book orders)
608 836-9000 (phone)
608 831-8200 (fax)
http://www.areditions.com

Matthew Jeffries

Consort, Full, and Verse Anthems

Edited by John Cannell

A-R Editions, Inc.
Madison

For Kelly, Thomas, and Emma

A-R Editions, Inc., Madison, Wisconsin 53717
© 1998 by A-R Editions, Inc.

Printed in the United States of America

ISBN 0-89579-413-6
ISSN 0484-123X

♾ The paper used in this publication meets the minimum requirements of the American National Standard for Information Sciences—Permanence of Paper for Printed Library Materials, ANSI Z39.48-1984.

Contents

Abbreviations and Sigla

Manuscripts

Great Britain

Cp 475–78	Cambridge, University Library, Peterhouse MSS 475–78 (the "Former Set")
Cp 487, 489–91	Cambridge, University Library, Peterhouse MSS 487, 489–91 (the "Latter Set")
Cp 493	Cambridge, University Library, Peterhouse MS 493
DRc A1, C2, C2*, C4–7, C9–11, C14–17, C19	Durham, Dean and Chapter Library, MSS C4, C5, C6, C7 second fascicle C9, C10 (Set 1); C2, C7 first fascicle, C14 (Set 5); C11, C16 (Set 6); A1, C2*, C15, C17, C19
GL 103, 105	Gloucester, Cathedral Library, unnumbered "Barnard" partbooks with additions [*Early English Church Music* reference numbers]
Lbl 17792–96	London, British Library, Additional MSS 17792–96
Lbl 29372–77	London, British Library, Additional MSS 29372–77 ("Tristitiae Remedium")
Lbl 30478–79	London, British Library, Additional MSS 30478–79
Lbl 6346	London, British Library, Harley MS 6346
Lcm 1045–51	London, Royal College of Music Library, MSS 1045–51 (the "Barnard" MS partbooks)
Lcm IA1	London, Royal College of Music Library, Printed Music I.A.1 with MS additions
Ob 23	Oxford, Bodleian Library, MS Rawl. Poet. 23 (the "Chapel Royal Anthem Book")
Ob Ten 791	Oxford, Bodleian Library, MS Tenbury 791 (the "Batten Organ Book")
Ob Ten 807–11	Oxford, Bodleian Library, MSS Tenbury 807–11
Och 56–60	Oxford, Christ Church Library, MSS Mus. 56–60
Och 1012	Oxford, Christ Church Library, MS Mus.1012
Och 1220–24	Oxford, Christ Church Library, MSS Mus.1220–24
Ojc 180	Oxford, St. John's College Library, Music MS 180
Y 29	York, Minster Library, MS M.29(S) (the "Dunnington-Jefferson" MS)

United States

NYp 4180–85	New York, The New York Public Library, Drexel MSS 4180–85
Ws 408	Washington, D.C., Folger Shakespeare Library, MS V.a.408

Publications

BCP 1560   *The Boke of Common Prayer . . . with The psalter or Psalmes of Dauyd . . .* (London, 1560) [British Library, pressmark C.25.h.12.]

BCP 1592   *The Booke of Common Prayer . . . with The Psalter or Psalmes of Dauid . . .* (London, 1592) [British Library, pressmark 3408.i.10.(1.)]

BCP   *The Book of Common Prayer*

Clifford 1663   James Clifford, *The Divine Services and Anthems usually sung in the Cathedrals and Collegiate Choires in the Church of England* (London, 1663) [British Library, pressmark C.110.b.17.]

Acknowledgments

Grateful acknowledgment is made to the following bodies for permission to publish this edition from manuscripts in their possession: the Master and Fellows of Peterhouse, Cambridge; the Dean and Chapter of Durham; the Dean and Chapter of Gloucester; the British Library; the Royal College of Music, London; the Music Division, The New York Public Library, Astor, Lenox, and Tilden Foundations; the Bodleian Library, Oxford; the Governing Body of Christ Church, Oxford; the President and Fellows of St. John's College, Oxford; the Folger Shakespeare Library, Washington, D.C.; and the York Minster Archives, by kind permission of the Dean and Chapter of York.

Extracts from the *Book of Common Prayer,* the rights of which are vested in the Crown, are reproduced by permission of the Crown's Patentee, Cambridge University Press.

Permission to publish biographical information contained in sources in the Cathedral Library has been granted by the Dean and Chapter of Wells. I am particularly indebted to the late Mr. L. S. Colchester, Honorary Archivist to the Dean and Chapter of Wells, and to his successor, Mrs. Frances Neale, for the information they have supplied.

I am very pleased to acknowledge the encouragement given by Mr. Leslie Hewitt, the extensive help and advice offered in so many ways by Dr. Ian Payne, and the support and encouragement of Jean, my wife, particularly when we were searching for historical and biographical material.

I should also like to thank the staff of all the libraries and Record Offices that I have consulted, particularly Mr. Richard Andrewes of the Cambridge University Library and the staff of the Pendlebury Library, Cambridge, for their help during my researches; Ms. Laetitia Yeandle of the Folger Shakespeare Library for her description of MS V.a.408; Dr. Robert Thompson for information about the Christ Church, Oxford sources; Mr. Peter A. Ward Jones of the Bodleian Library for his help with biographical material; Mr. Brian Crosby for information about the Durham Cathedral music manuscripts; and, finally, Professor Peter Aston of the University of East Anglia, Norwich, for his advice about the music of George Jeffreys and possible errors of attribution. Any errors or misinterpretations, however, are my responsibility alone.

Introduction

The Composer

Very little has been discovered about the private life of Matthew Jeffries; no information has come to light about his date and place of birth, his parents, his possible marriage and offspring, or his death.[1]

Rather more is known of his professional life from documents preserved at Wells Cathedral, but even these rarely give an insight into the characters of the people involved. Many only summarize the place and purpose of a meeting, and list who attended and the duties allocated to some of them. The first mention of Jeffries occurs in the Act Book of the Vicars Choral, dated 28 December 1579, where it states that in the Vicars' Hall, "Matthew Jefferies, just admitted Vicar Choral of the Cathedral Church of Wells on a year's probation, took the corporal oath, touching the holy gospels of God, to keep inviolably the Statutes of this New Close." This would suggest that he was born around 1558, the year of Elizabeth I's accession, and would therefore be roughly contemporary with Thomas Morley and Nathaniel Giles, and slightly younger than Edmund Hooper and Elway Bevin.

When Matthew Jeffries was appointed as a Vicar Choral, or singingman, in Wells Cathedral, the English reformation was well established and there is nothing to suggest that he, like the majority of his countrymen, was anything but a loyal adherent of the reformed church. It has been suggested that his colleague, Elway Bevin, a composer and theorist of Welsh origin, was a life-long, but probably secret, Catholic. Certainly Bevin and a senior Vicar Choral, Thomas Gould, were temporarily suspended by the Dean and Chapter of Wells for not having received Holy Communion for four years.[2]

Each year in the Vicars' Hall on the feast of St. Matthew (21 September) the Vicars Choral met to elect "the Principals and other officials of the New Close of the Vicars of Wells." In 1585 Jeffries was elected to the post of Receiver General, which meant that for that year he would, presumably by prior arrangement, sit in the Chequer, a room built above the main staircase, to receive the rent and other dues from the tenants of properties owned by the Vicars Choral.[3] Incidentally, the New Close is another name for the Vicars' Close, being new in 1382. In 1583 the lease of one of these properties was granted to seven of the younger Vicars Choral, including Jeffries and Bevin. It was made up of "a tenement, five stables, an orchard and a garden, in La Montroye Lane" (within the area of the city known as The Liberty), and provided a yearly income of 32s 8d for the Vicars' common fund.[4]

The musical establishment at Wells at this time consisted of six choristers and fourteen Vicars Choral. Of the fourteen men, normally all but the two Principals were laymen, with five being classed as Seniors. An Organist and a Master of the Choristers were appointed from among the Vicars Choral by the Dean and Chapter. Jeffries is first named as Master of the Choristers in an account roll for 1587–88, when John Clerke was Organist, and was allowed £29 19s 4d for the year from various sources for the maintenance of the choristers. He also received 20 shillings for the repair of books.[5]

The Communar's Paper Account Book for 1591 and 1592 contains the signatures of the Vicars Choral when receiving their quarterly allowances of fifteen shillings. Several of the more senior members also received various *ex gratia* payments, such as 3s 4d to Robert Marwood for carrying letters. Jeffries received five shillings, again for the repair of books. Unfortunately, there are many breaks in the accounts, with a very substantial gap occurring between 1601 and 1633, by which time Jeffries' name no longer appears. However, in October 1591 and again in October 1592, Jeffries accepted annual payments of £9 19s 4d on behalf of the Choristers, for which he himself signed (see fig. 1).[6]

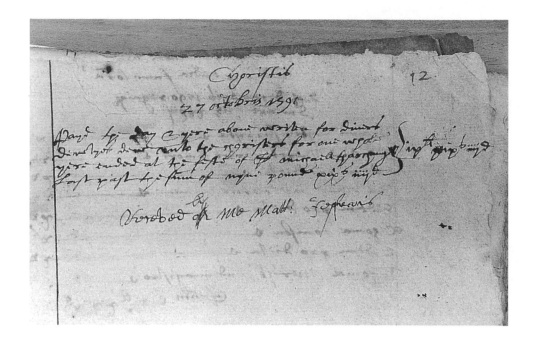

Figure 1. Matthew Jeffries' signature; Wells Cathedral Library, "Communar's Paper Account Book 1591–92," fol. 12r. (Reproduced by permission of the Dean and Chapter of Wells)

Choristis
27 octobris 1591
Payd the day & yere above writen for Divers
Dewtyes dew unto the choristers for one whole
yere ended at the feste of St michaell tharchangel } ix^{li} xix^s iiij^d
last past the sum[m] of nyne pound[es] xix^s iiij^d
Receved of by Me Matt: Jefferis

In 1590, it seems that some of the Vicars Choral wrote to the Attorney General and Her Majesty's Solicitor asking that they might sever themselves from the jurisdiction of the Dean and Chapter of Wells, inferring that this action had the approval of all the Vicars. Seven Vicars Choral, including Jeffries, obviously disagreed, writing that they were quite content to "remaine under the good and quiett goverment of the saide Deane and Chapter." Nevertheless, the Vicars Choral continued to seek clarification of their relationship with the Dean and Chapter, particularly with regard to extra duties or "offices" and the associated fees and emoluments. It was at this time, in the fall of 1593, that Jeffries' name first appeared among the Senior Vicars. One of the duties that Jeffries was given from time to time was that of "Hearer" (presumably a voice coach) for newly appointed Vicars Choral, such as Timothy Green in 1585 and William Tawswell, a tenor, in 1588. Green was perpetuated the next year, but when Jeffries sought the perpetuation of Tawswell after his year of probation was completed, the Chapter rejected him

out of hand, even though the Vicars had found him satisfactory in behavior, skill, and voice.[7]

On 25 February 1593/94 Jeffries, described in *Fasti Oxonienses* as "Matthew Jeffrye Vicar choral in the Church at Wells," was admitted B.Mus. at Oxford University in company with Arthur Cock, Organist of Exeter Cathedral and later, for a short time, of the Chapel Royal.[8]

Many of Jeffries' colleagues were accused, and often convicted, of various offenses by the Dean and Chapter, but Jeffries seems to have been largely innocent of any misbehavior. However, on 20 November 1600 all "the vicars-choral, except John Hulett and Richard Mason, appeared and confessed that it was true that on Wednesday at evening prayers only four of them were present. They were admonished to be more diligent, and not to frequent taverns nor walk the streets." The previous month, William Tawswell (who had eventually been perpetuated in 1593) was "accused of incontinence with Mary, wife of Robert Marwood." In November 1607, John Corne, a Vicar Choral, was charged, and witnesses confirmed, that he used "very unreverent wordes of the canons of this church, viz. that he cared not a fart for any of the doctors of this church." In 1599 the Communar was forbidden "to pay to Thomas Gould and John Hulett any of their quotidians as from October 1 until they shall receive the Holy Communion in the cathedral, according to the order of October 12, 1598."[9] John Hewlett, and possibly Thomas Gould, were by then members of the Chapel Royal, so that their attendance at Wells was intermittent. The men of the Chapel Royal attended the Monarch every other month on a revolving basis, except on special occasions, when all 32 Gentlemen were needed. The rota system would have allowed Hewlett and Gould to have sung in the choir at Wells and to have earned their stipend as promised by the Chapter.[10] A journey of 125 miles each way on horseback would not have been a pleasing prospect, however, especially in the winter months.

When Thomas Gould came to prepare his will in July 1608, he asked that he be buried, because of his long service to the Cathedral, in the aisle by the old clock, and promised "to every Vicar Chorall that shall accompany my Corps to the grave in their Habitts twelve pence a peece, and to my olde good freinde Mr Mathewe Jefferis tenn shillinges over and above his Twelve pence, in toto Eleaven shillinges, and to every Chorister Sixe pence a peece."[11]

The last mention of Jeffries that has come to light in the Wells Cathedral archives is dated 16 December 1613, and records that Jeffries was in dispute with the Archdeacon of Wells, Dr. Gerard Wood. It appears, although no precise details are given, that Jeffries had spoken rudely to the Archdeacon at the presentation of a new Vicar [Choral]. Jeffries, appearing before the Chapter, admitted his offense and Dr. Wood accepted his apology.[12] On 2 March 1617/18 Walter Tailer is described as Master of the Choristers, so it would seem that Jeffries had either died or left the service of the Cathedral some time between the end of 1613 and early 1618.[13] No Cathedral registers of burials survive from this time, and the editor has been unable to locate any will of Jeffries, either at the Somerset Record Office, or at the Public Record Office, London, which holds those proved at the Prerogative Court of Canterbury.

Anthony Wood suggests, in his notes on musicians, that George Jeffreys was "descended as it seems from the former Matthew," but the editor has been unable to find anything further to support this rather tentative statement.[14]

Wells Cathedral

Mention should be made of the Cathedral Church of St. Andrew in Wells, a magnificent Gothic building commenced about 1180 and completed in all essentials by 1508. Wells is a city of some 9,400 inhabitants, near the Mendip Hills in the county of Somerset in England's West Country. Virtually all the main structure of the cathedral remains as Jeffries would have known it. Even the massive and modern-looking scissor-arches, built to support the tower when the foundations of two piers sank, were in place two centuries before Jeffries was born. On the west wall of the north transept is the second-oldest working clock in the world, complete with jousting knights and Jack Blandiver, who strikes the bells for the quarter hours with his heels and the hour bell with his hammer. This clock was made before 1392, and, although it has been repaired and repainted at various times, has been kept going through the centuries.

Not just the cathedral, but nearly all the surrounding buildings, including the Bishop's Palace, the Old Deanery, the "Bishop's Eye" gatehouse, the Vicars' Hall, and the Vicars' Close were all built long before Jeffries' time, and in all essentials have hardly changed since. The houses of Vicars' Close have been occupied by the Vicars Choral, the men of the Cathedral choir, from 1382 to the present day. The Vicars' Hall, dating from 1348, was used both as a dining hall and for meetings of the Vicars Choral, where annually they elected officers from among their number.[15]

The Music

The Chapel Royal, where the wishes of Queen Elizabeth I were paramount, was always high-church, almost Catholic, in ceremonial, and was a center of excellence in both musical composition and performance. This preeminence continued under her Stuart successors. Gradually, the works of the Chapel Royal composers spread into the repertory of the provincial cathedrals and collegiate chapels, in turn influencing the provincial composers to emulate their style.

Jeffries' style must have been largely formed by the last decade of Elizabeth's reign, and shares many of the features of the works of William Byrd's younger contemporaries Edmund Hooper and Elway Bevin, as well as of Byrd himself. The works of these composers include such peculiarly English traits as juxtaposed major and minor tonalities, simultaneous major and minor thirds, and various forms of English cadence. This latter is characterized by the simultaneous sounding of the flattened seventh with the tonic, before the tonic descends to the leading note, as in no. 2, measure 12. Other variants of this cadence, with a scalewise descent from the flattened seventh, and with the major seventh, can be seen in no. 1, measure 17 and no. 6, measure 43.

Jeffries seems particularly happy writing in six parts, where he is able to vary the texture by resting one or other of the parts for a few measures. In the consort anthems, effective contrasts are made between the elaborate, quasi-canonic writing of the verse sections and the broad, sonorous homophony of the following chorus, which, in turn, expands into counterpoint. Often the chorus moves on to the next verse of the text, but, at certain key points, the chorus takes up the material of the soloists and expands it.

An essential feature of Byrd's anthems is his unrivalled use of tonality in the overall shaping of the music. Jeffries also uses passing modulations and abrupt changes of "key" effectively, but perhaps not with the structural skill of Byrd. Jeffries' liking for imitative passages based on a descending scale or arpeggio, a fifth in extent, usually produces a descent through the "keys": for examples of this "modulatory" tendency, see no. 10, measures 23–30, and no. 11, measures 151–59. In the first of these examples the process is interrupted dramatically by a sudden shift from B-flat major to G major. A close on the dominant major, followed, after a rest, by a major chord on the minor mediant is one of the abrupt "key" changes favored by Jeffries. Unlike his contemporary Nathaniel Giles, however, Jeffries never writes extended chromatic passages.

The works of Jeffries included in this volume are of three types: consort, full, and verse anthems. Consort and verse anthems are closely related, with the contrast between solo voices and chorus an essential feature of both. Consort anthems were conceived as domestic music to be performed in the houses of the nobility and gentry, or at court. Often, although not in the settings by Jeffries, the texts were contemporary devotional verse of no great merit. These anthems are scored for voices and viols, with, presumably, one voice and one instrument to a part. It is usually assumed that the instruments play throughout. Verse anthems were written for liturgical use, using biblical or prayer book texts, and feature one or more soloists, accompanied by the organ, alternating with passages for the full cathedral choir. The organ played throughout, supplying an independent part in the verse sections. Jeffries' verse anthem, "Praise the Lord, the God of Might," was obviously written for a special royal occasion, and therefore a setting of a non-liturgical text was acceptable. Where music and text were suitable, consort anthems were converted into verse anthems by providing an organ part to replace the viols. The anthem "If the Lord Himself" is an example of such a transfer. Full anthems, as can be seen from their sources, were performed in both domestic and liturgical environments, but in the latter case, only if the text were suitable.

The choirs of cathedrals and collegiate chapels were (and still are) divided into two groups, *decani* and *cantoris*, each with the capability of providing two contratenor parts. The two groups face each other, with the *decani* choir usually to the south, and the *cantoris* to the north. When performing the canticles and other service music, the two choirs often sing antiphonally, but this occurs less frequently with anthems. Each of the mens' parts, typically performed by two singers, would have been sung from a single partbook, with a chosen soloist singing the passages marked "verse." In an anthem requiring two tenor parts, for example, one part would be sung by the tenor decani singers, the other by the tenor cantoris.

Matthew Jeffries was far from a prolific composer, even though several of his works are now lost. Neither would it appear that he composed in many genres; he seemingly wrote no madrigals, keyboard works, or Latin motets, for example. He did, however, compose Anglican service music and consort music for viols, in addition to the consort, full, and verse anthems. The uppermost part of four works for viols, including two In Nomines, are to be found in Ws 408, but sadly, no other parts survive. The organ part and portions of a bass part of a large-scale "Morning and Evening Service for Means" are preserved at Durham, and three cantoris partbooks of Jeffries' smaller-scale First and Second Services survive.[16] Unfortunately, nothing remains of those passages sung by the decani choir alone. The Magnificat and Nunc Dimittis of the Second Service, which have no antiphonal sections, could conceivably be reconstructed. They apparently lack two upper voice parts, however.

Of the twelve anthems given in this edition, six— three consort (nos. 1, 2, 3) and three full anthems (nos. 8, 9, 10)—are complete. The remaining anthems, of which one part at least is lacking, have been reconstructed by the editor.

The three consort anthems appear to be modeled on William Byrd's "Christ Rising Again / Christ Is Risen," which was published in 1589, but, from the number of Jacobean sources surviving, was still popular in the early seventeenth century. The scoring, using six voices, two mean soloists, and viols, is identical with that of Byrd's anthem. Again, like Byrd, Jeffries often rests an upper voice in the initial short "choral" passages, conserving his full resources to the greatest effect in an extended final chorus and Amen. Furthermore, the opening idea of "If the Lord Himself" would seem to allude to the opening accompaniment figure of "Christ Rising Again."

"My Song Shall Be Alway" is a rather unusual anthem in that each section opens with an ensemble verse, followed by an extended eight-part chorus. It could be argued that, although no organ part now exists, it should be classed as a verse anthem. In those source partbooks which have an original table (Lcm

1049 and 1051), however, it is included among the full anthems, probably because it requires no independent organ accompaniment. Orlando Gibbons' anthem "Hosanna to the Son of David," where the opening and other passages are often marked "verse" in the sources, is a similar case, and is certainly listed consistently in the sources as a full anthem. An interesting comparison can be made between Jeffries' setting of "Out of the Deep" with the verse settings of the same text by Thomas Morley and Nathaniel Giles, particularly at the words "O Lord, who may abide it?"

None of the sources of Jeffries' anthems contains any explicit dating information. However, the date of Ws 408, although not precise, suggests that the five-part anthems nos. 6 and 7 were written in the late 1580s or early 1590s. A factor which may assist in dating some of the anthems is that James Montague, who became Dean of the Chapel Royal in 1603, was, in addition, installed as Bishop of Bath and Wells in 1608.[17] Jeffries almost certainly saw this as an opportunity for professional advancement, so it seems quite likely that the consort anthems (nos. 1, 2, 3) and the non-liturgical anthems (nos. 5 and 8) were written for performance in the Bishop's Palace at Wells when Bishop Montague was in residence.

After the failure of the Gunpowder Plot on 5 November 1605, a thanksgiving service was instituted "for the happy deliuerance of his Maiestie, the Queene, Prince, and States of Parliament, from the most Traiterous and bloody intended Massacre."[18] Although not a designated psalm for the service, Psalm 124, "If the Lord Himself," seems, nevertheless, to have become associated with this annual thanksgiving. Certainly a verse setting of this psalm by Edward Smith is listed in the table of Y 29 under "The Fift of November." This would suggest that Jeffries' setting of Psalm 124 (no. 1) was written after 1605, and probably after 1608. Bishop Montague may well have encouraged Jeffries to write his verse anthem "Praise the Lord, the God of Might" for performance in the Chapel Royal, in whose Anthem Book can be found a version of the text. This anthem was certainly written in the reign of James I, being described by Clifford as "a prayer for the King, and the Royal Family" and includes the phrase "Our King, Queen, Prince." It may, of course, have been written for performance at Wells in August 1613, when Queen Anne visited the city during her tour of the West Country, and later adopted by the Chapel Royal.[19]

While most of the partbooks attribute these anthems to "Matthew Jeffries" or to "Mr. Jeffries of Wells," some have simply "Mr. Jeffries." This begs the question, could some works be by George Jeffreys? Although in his mature works George Jeffreys writes in an Italianate baroque style, it is possible that apprentice works by

him were composed in the older polyphonic fashion. Of the anthems not positively attributed to Matthew, two (nos. 6 and 11) would seem to occur in sources too early to be by George, leaving doubts only about the four-part anthem "Praise the Lord, O Ye Servants." This anthem, however, displays some characteristics typical of Matthew, notably the passage setting the words "unto the going down of the same" (mm. 35–40).[20]

The Texts

The first *Book of Common Prayer* had been issued under Edward VI in 1549 to supply, in the vernacular, the texts for all the services and offices of the Church of England, thereby replacing the many Latin service manuals previously used. A second, more Calvinist, *Book of Common Prayer* was issued in 1552 and became in 1559 the basis for Elizabeth's prayer book, which, however, avoided a few of the extremes of 1552.

The texts of the nine psalm settings (and seven incipits in the appendix) of this edition are essentially those given in *The Book of Common Prayer* as published in the reign of Charles II in 1662 and reprinted, with minor modifications, up to the present day. Jeffries, however, worked from earlier texts, and examination of two prayer books from the reign of Elizabeth (*BCP* 1560 and *BCP* 1592) shows that there are several textual differences in the earlier Psalters. Other minor variants and additions to the text would seem to have been introduced by Jeffries himself. The allocation of "Proper Psalms" for various festivals of the Church is different in the earlier prayer books from those of the later editions. The Psalter of *BCP* 1592 was found a more reliable source than *BCP* 1560 which sometimes gives a corrupted text. The copies consulted are listed in the abbreviations and sigla. The use of certain psalms for festivals and various textual differences and additions are listed in the critical notes. The spelling, punctuation, and capitalization of the psalm texts in the edition follow recent editions of *BCP*.

The partbooks are the only known source of the texts of the non-liturgical anthems, and in neither case has the identity of the author been discovered. The single stanza of "My Love Is Crucified" consists of six iambic pentameters, while the text of "In Thee, O Lord, Do I Trust" appears to be a paraphrase of Psalm 31:1,18. In both cases the spelling has been modernized, and punctuation and capitalization have been added by the editor.

The text of "Praise the Lord, the God of Might" is found in three sources. The earliest of these, the "Chapel Royal Anthem Book" (Ob 23), gives the fourth line of verse three as "Keep them in peace sans trouble and distress" which neither scans properly nor fits the music. Also, unlike all the partbooks (Och 1220–24, Ojc 180, and Ob Ten 791), the same choral refrain is used for all three verses. Clifford 1663, on the other hand, agrees closely with those parts of the text given in the surviving voice parts. He does, however, omit the line "The Son that it redeem'd and saved," as does his second edition of 1664. Lbl 6346, the third source, dating from the late seventeenth century, appears to be a copy of Ob 23. Slight doubts are raised regarding the authorship by the attribution of this anthem in Ob 23 (and Lbl 6346) to "W Jeffrye." Och 1220, 1221, and 1223 attribute the anthem to "Mr Mathew Jeffries," however, and Ob Ten 791 ascribes it to "Mr Jeffreis of Wells." Clifford and the other part-books have either "Mr. Jefferies" or no attribution. Clifford 1663 has been used as the source of the text, with the spelling modernized and punctuation and capitalization added in a few places by the editor. Minor textual variants are recorded in the critical notes.

Notes on Performance

The anthems in this edition use the original note values and are notated at the original pitch. The use of the former should not be thought to imply slow tempos, however. Tempos should be flexible, but will depend to some extent on the characteristics of the building used for the performance. The majority of the pieces can be transposed up a whole tone with advantage. Some, such as "In Thee, O Lord," the two parts of "My Song Shall Be Alway," and "Praise the Lord, the God of Might," would benefit from being transposed up a minor third. The absence of dynamic indications is intended to give the performers freedom to apply their own ideas of dynamic expression, not to imply a constant mezzo forte.

In the consort anthems, viols would provide the most suitable instrumental accompaniment, but, in their absence, modern stringed instruments, played with discretion, are acceptable. Cornetts and sackbuts or a mixed consort of string and wind instruments could prove interesting, providing a satisfactory balance can be achieved. The organ part of "If the Lord himself" should be used as an alternative to strings or winds, not to supplement them. The use of the organ part of "Rejoice in the Lord, O Ye Righteous" is optional, as the anthem can be satisfactorily performed unaccompanied. Organ registrations should take account of the resources that were available to sixteenth- and seventeenth-century English organists.

The consort anthems, when performed with strings, are probably most satisfactory with one voice and one instrument to a part, but if performed with organ or cornetts and sackbuts, the "choral" sections can be sung with two or three voices to a part. All "verse" sections should preferably be sung with one solo voice to a part. The complement of singers at Wells Cathedral at the end of the sixteenth century would suggest that each side of the choir had three boy means, three contratenors, two tenors, and two basses. While the names of the singingmen are known, their types of voice have, except in a very few cases, unfortunately not come down to us.

In the consort anthems, also it will be noticed that Jeffries often overlaps the beginning of a "verse" section with the end of the preceding "full" section. Here, the editor believes, the partbooks show the instrumental parts rather than what is meant for the singers. Singing what is given in the sources, the final notes of the full section will arrive together, but end in a ragged fashion in different parts of the measure. The need may therefore be felt to adjust the length of the last note of some of the vocal parts of these "full" sections. For example, the final chord of the "full" section of "If the Lord Himself" at measure 84 could be sung as a semibreve by all voices, with the instrumental parts being played as written. There is support for this idea in the Och partbooks, where, at measure 44 of "Sing We Merrily," fermatas are placed over the minims of the contratenor and sextus parts at "day." Similarly in "Out of the Deep" at measure 59, a fermata is placed over the tenor (but not the contratenor part) at "watch."

Notes

1. A search of the *International Genealogical Index* (produced by the Church of Jesus Christ of the Latter Day Saints) for the English and Welsh counties reveals only two of a suitable date: a "Matthewe Geffreis" was baptized on 21 September 1560 (St. Matthew's day) at Pattingham in Staffordshire, and a "Mathewe Geofferye" married Alyce Eglestone on 17 June 1571 at St. Giles' Church in Reading. Nothing further on either could be found, and there is nothing to link either with the composer.

2. W. P. Baildon, ed., *Calendar of the Manuscripts of the Dean and Chapter of Wells,* Historical Manuscripts Commission, vol. 2 (London, 1914), 302. For Bevin, see H. Watkins Shaw, *The Succession of Organists* (Oxford, 1991), 36–37.

3. L. S. Colchester, ed., "Act Book 1541–1593 of the Vicars Choral of Wells," (Unpublished typescript, Wells, 1986), 41–57. Copy in Wells Cathedral Library.

4. Baildon, *Calendar,* Charter 799, p. 709.

5. L. S. Colchester, ed., "Communars' Accounts 1327–1600," (Unpublished typescript, Wells, 1984), 293. Copy in Wells Cathedral Library. For John Clerke and the musical establishment at Wells, see Watkins Shaw, *Succession,* 283–85.

6. Dean and Chapter Archives, Wells Cathedral Library, "Communar's Paper Account Book 1591–92," fols. 10r–12r, 25r–27r. The remaining twenty pounds not listed in the account, making up a total of £29 19s 4d, came from a bequest from the Vicar of St. Cuthbert's Church in Wells, and was obviously paid separately.

7. Colchester, "Act Book," 46–51, 56.

8. Anthony Wood, *Fasti Oxonienses,* vol. 1, 1500–1640 (London, 1691), column 770. This volume is included in Anthony Wood, *Athenae Oxonienses,* vol. 2, 1500–1690 (London, 1691, 92). On Arthur Cock, see Ian Payne, "Two Early Organists of Exeter Cathedral," *Devon and Cornwall Notes and Queries* 35 (1983): 133–42. See also Watkins Shaw, *Succession,* 5–6, 45.

9. Baildon, *Calendar,* 340–41, 354.

10. Baildon, *Calendar,* 313.

11. Public Record Office, London, "Prerogative Court of Canterbury Wills," PROB 11/112, 227RH–228LH.

12. Dean and Chapter Archives, Wells Cathedral Library, "Chapter Act Book Vol. K, 1607–21," fol. 79v.

13. Baildon, *Calendar,* 374.

14. Bodleian Library, Oxford, "MS. Wood D.19(4)" (ca. 1695), fol. 72r.

15. L. S. Colchester, *Wells Cathedral* (London, 1987).

16. The sources for the "Morning and Evening Service for Means" are GB-DRc MS A2 (organ) and DRc MS C18 (bassus decani) and for the First and Second Services are GB-Mp MS 340 Cr 71 (altus cantoris), GL 105 (tenor cantoris), and Lcm IA1 (bassus cantoris). In addition, the Te Deum of the First Service is given in GB-Och MS Mus. 1246 (tenor [cantoris]).

17. Peter Le Huray, *Music and the Reformation in England 1549–1660* (London, 1967), 59–60. See also Baildon, *Calendar,* 356.

18. The full title of the prayer book for the service on 5 November is *Prayers and Thanksgiuing to bee vsed by all the Kings Maiesties louing Subiects, for the happy deliuerance of his Maiestie, the Queene, Prince, and States of Parliament, from the most Traiterous and bloody intended Massacre by Gunpowder, the fift of Nouember 1605. Set forth by Authority.* (London, 1610?) [British Library, pressmark 3406.c.41.] The Proper Psalms listed for the Service are Psalms 35, 68, and 69.

19. T. Scott Holmes, *Wells and Glastonbury, a historical and topographical account* (London, 1908), 120–21. Queen Anne, the consort of James I, was the sister of King Christian IV of Denmark.

20. Professor Peter Aston of the University of East Anglia, an authority on the music of George Jeffreys, examined this anthem (no. 4) and thought it very unlikely to be by George Jeffreys (personal communication to the editor).

Texts

The texts of the verses of the psalms are to be found in the *Book of Common Prayer*. Given here are the texts of those anthems which set anonymous verse or prose.

5. My Love Is Crucified

My love is crucified, dead and entombed,
Raised up, ascended, fixed on heav'ns high throne,
Whence it shall ne'er descend to be enwombed
In mortal mould. Christ is my love alone,
My heart, my tongue, my hand are at his call,
All else is naught, Christ is my all in all.

8. In Thee, O Lord, Do I Trust

In thee, O Lord, do I trust; therefore shall I not be confounded for ever. Deliver me in thy righteousness, I beseech thee, my God. Cast a cheerful countenance upon thy servant, for thy Name's sake. Amen.

12. Praise the Lord, the God of Might

A prayer for the King, and the Royal Family.

Praise the Lord, the God of might and power
For all the wonders he hath done;
O magnify the Son our Saviour,

Give laud unto that Holy One,
Proceeding from the Father and the Son:

With instruments of melody,
Sing praises to the Trinity.

The God that heav'n and earth hath made
And all things in the world of naught;
The Son, that it redeem'd and saved,
And us from hell and darkness bought;
He that our hearts hath newly wrought:

With instruments of melody,
Sing praises to the Trinity.

That Godhead which these three conjoins,
Our King, Queen, Prince preserve and bless:
Bless them all that spring from their loins,
Keep them in peace without distress:
Bear up their friends, their foes depress:

So shall we all sing joyfully,
Praise to his holy Majesty. Amen.

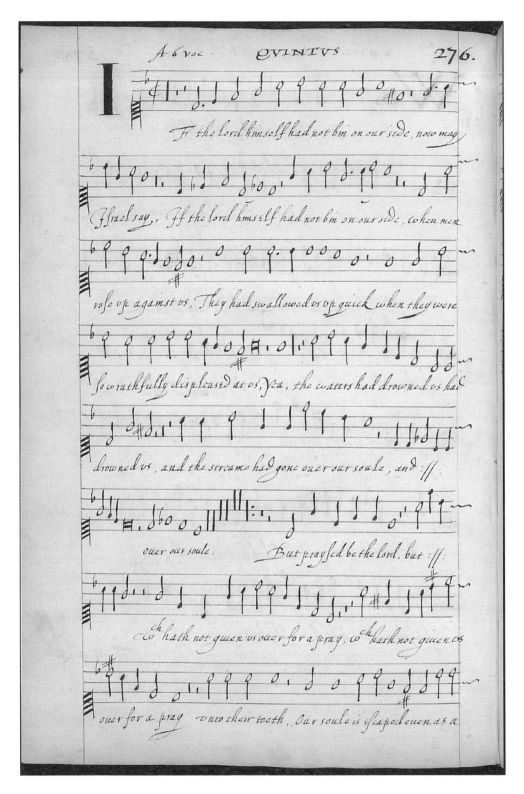

Plate 1. "If the Lord Himself," quintus partbook; London, British Library, Additional MS 29376, fol. 130v. (Reproduced by permission of the British Library)

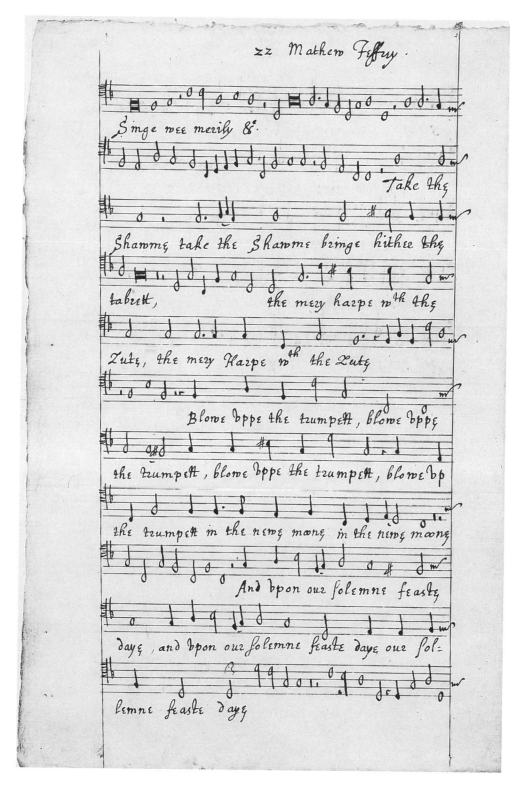

Plate 2. "Sing We Merrily," sextus partbook; Oxford, Christ Church Library, MS Mus. 58, p. 22. (Reproduced by permission of the Governing Body of Christ Church, Oxford)

Plate 3. "Rejoice in the Lord, O Ye Righteous," [contratenor cantoris] partbook; Durham, Dean and Chapter Library, MS C7, p. 122. (Reproduced by permission of the Dean and Chapter of Durham)

Consort Anthems

1. If the Lord Himself

Psalm 124:1–7

12

Our help stand- eth in the Name of the Lord:

Our help stand- eth in the Name of

Verse

which hath made heav'n and earth, hea⟨v'n and earth.⟩

the Lord: which hath made heav'n and earth. Our ⟨help stand- eth

Our help stand- eth

Our help stand- eth

Our help stand- eth

Our help stand- eth

Chorus

14

2. Out of the Deep

Psalm 130:1–7

20

-demp- ti - on, re- demp- ti- on. A- -

is plen- te- ous re- demp- ti- on. A-

-ous re- demp- ti- on, re- demp- - ti- on. _____

-demp- ti- on, re- demp- ti- on.

-on, is plen- te- ous re- demp-ti- on. A- - men,

and with him is plen- te- ous re- demp- ti- on. A-

-men, A- men.

- [men, A- - men.]

A- - - men.

A- - men, A- men.

A- - - men.

- [men, A]- men.

24

3. Sing We Merrily

Psalm 81:1–4

Sing we mer-ri-ly un-to God our strength, sing we mer-ri-ly un-to God our strength: make a cheer-ful

noise, make a cheer-ful noise un- to the God of Ja- cob.

Take —

Take —

Take —

Take —

Take —

the mer- ry

— the psalm, take the psalm, bring hith- er the tab- ret:

— the psalm, take the psalm, bring hith- er the tab- ret:

— the psalm, take the psalm, bring hith- er the tab- ret:

— the psalm, take the ___ psalm, bring hith- er the tab- ret: ___

— the psalm, take the psalm, bring hith- er the tab- ret:

28

Full Anthems

4. Praise the Lord, O Ye Servants

Psalm 113:1–5

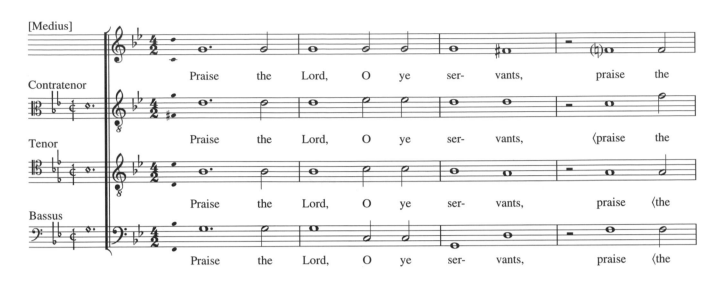

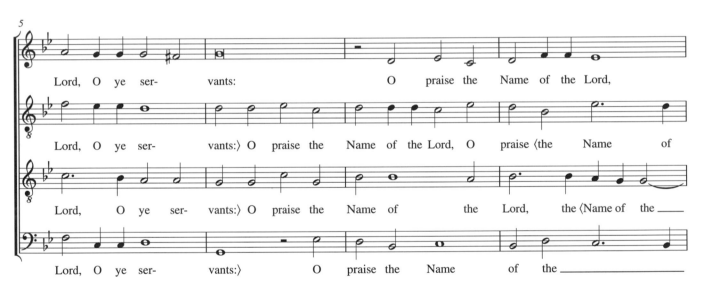

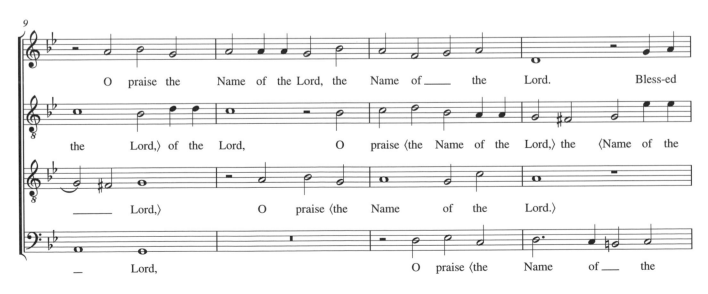

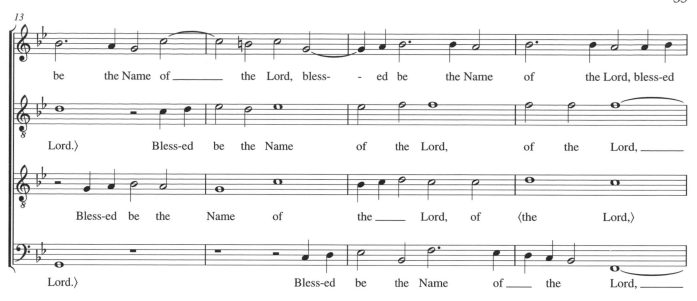

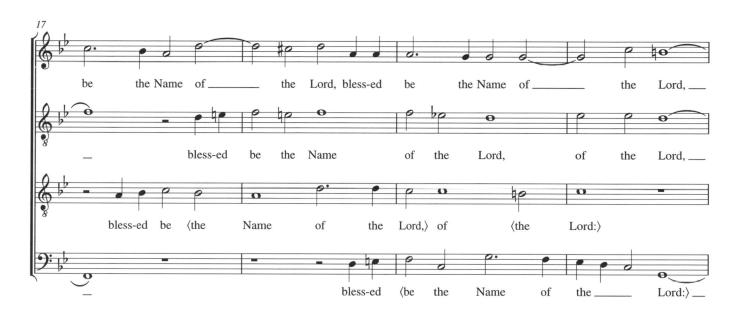

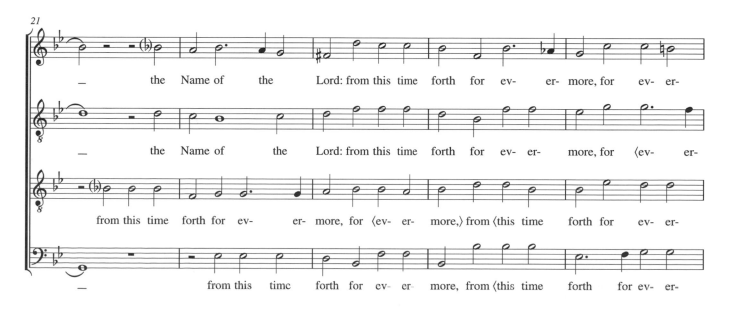

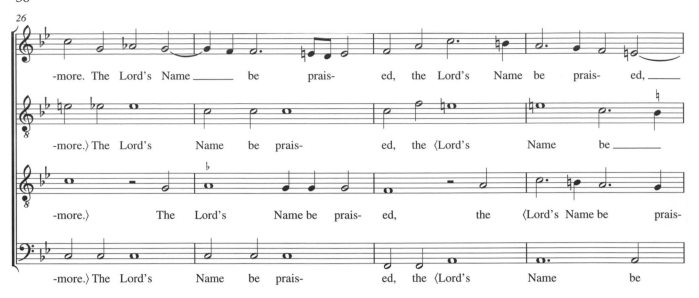

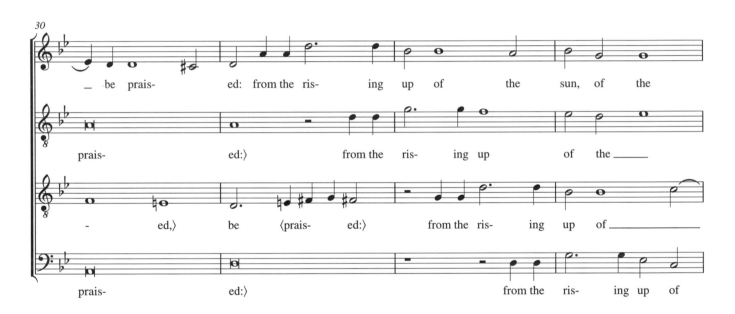

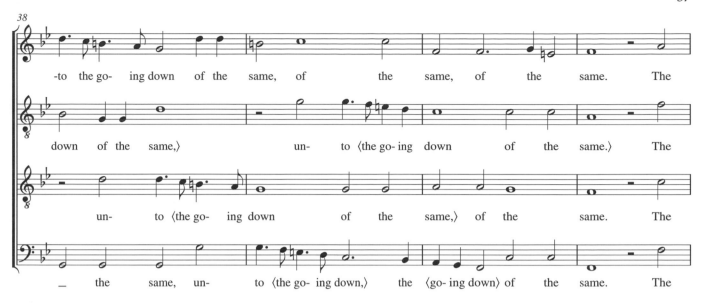

-to the go- ing down of the same, of the same, of the same. The

down of the same,⟩ un- to ⟨the go- ing down of the same.⟩ The

un- to ⟨the go- ing down of the same,⟩ of the same. The

_ the same, un- to ⟨the go- ing down,⟩ the ⟨go- ing down⟩ of the same. The

Lord is high a- bove all hea- then: and his glo- ry a- bove the heav'ns. Who is

Lord is high a- bove all hea- then: and his glo- ry a- bove the heav'ns. Who is

Lord is high a- bove all hea- then: and his glo- ry a- bove the heav'ns. Who is

Lord is high a- bove all hea- then: and his glo- ry a- bove the heav'ns. Who is

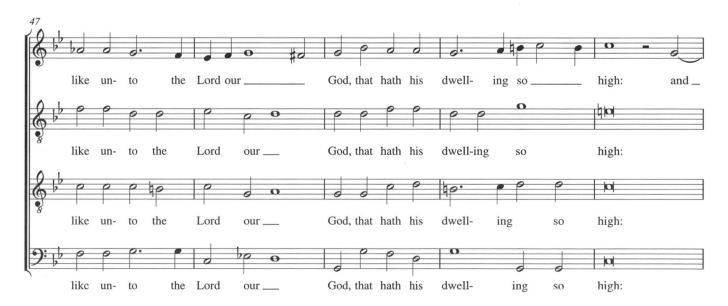

like un- to the Lord our _____ God, that hath his dwell- ing so _____ high: and _

like un- to the Lord our _ God, that hath his dwell-ing so high:

like un- to the Lord our _ God, that hath his dwell- ing so high:

like un- to the Lord our _ God, that hath his dwell- ing so high:

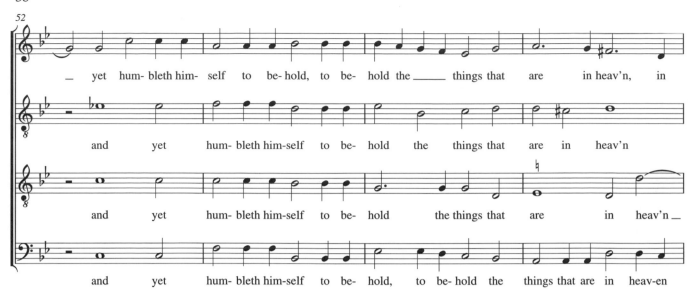

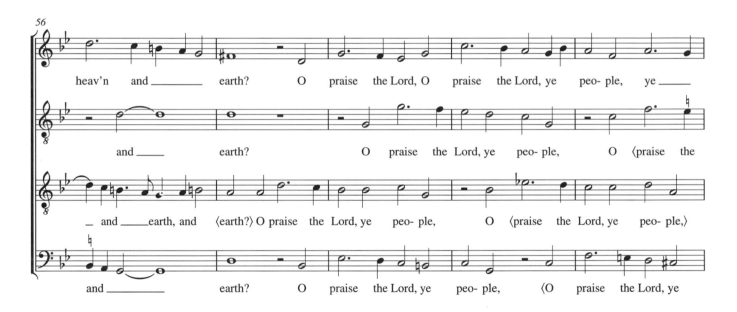

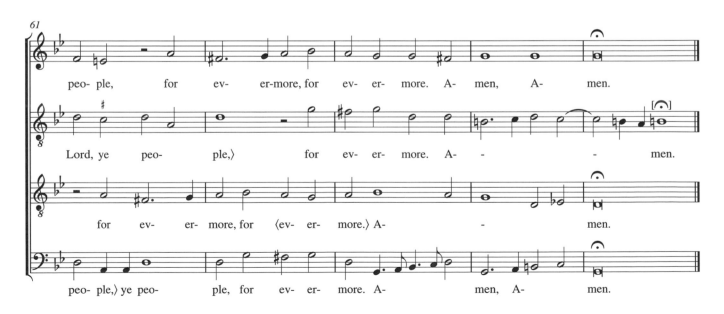

5. My Love Is Crucified

40

44

6. Praise the Lord, Ye Servants

Psalm 113:1–4

48

50

7. Sing We Merrily

Psalm 81:1–4

⟨the mer- ry harp with ⎯ the lute,⟩ ⟨the mer- ry harp with the lute.⟩ Blow

the ⎯ lute, with the lute, ⎯⎯⎯ the mer- ry harp with the lute.

the ⎯ lute, the mer- ry harp with the ⎯ lute, the mer- ry harp with the ⎯ lute.

with the lute, the mer- ry harp with the lute, the mer- ry harp with the lute.

the ⎯ lute, the mer- ry harp with the ⎯ lute, the mer- ry harp with the ⎯ lute.

up the trum- pet, ⟨blow up the trum- pet,⟩ the trum- pet, ⟨the

Blow up the trum- pet, the trum- pet,

Blow up the trum- pet, blow up ⎯⎯⎯ the trum- pet, the trum- pet,

Blow up the trum- pet, blow up ⎯⎯⎯ the trum- pet, the trum- pet,

Blow up the trum- pet, blow up ⎯⎯⎯ the trum- pet, the trum- pet,

-on our sol- - emn feast- day.⟩ For this was made a stat- ute,

and up- on our sol-emn feast- day, sol- - emn feast- day. For

and up- on our sol-emn feast- day, our sol-emn feast- day. For this was made a

and up- on our sol-emn feast- day, our sol-emn feast- day. For this was made a stat-

and up- on our sol-emn feast- day, our sol-emn feast- day.

⟨for this was made a stat- ute,⟩ ⟨for

this was made a stat- ute, a stat- - ute, a stat-

stat- ute, for this was made a stat- ute, a stat-

-ute, a stat- ute, a stat- ute, for this was made a stat-

For this was made a stat- ute, for this was made a stat-

8. In Thee, O Lord, Do I Trust

I be-⟨seech thee, my _____ God.⟩ Cast _____

Cast a cheer-ful coun- te- nance up- on thy ser- vant,

_ a cheer-ful coun- te- nance up- on thy _____ ser- vant,

_ God.⟩ _____ Cast _____ a cheer- ful coun- te- nance

thee, my God,⟩ O my God. Cast a cheer-ful coun- te-

_____ God. Cast a cheer-ful coun- te- nance up-on thy ser- vant,

_ a cheer- ful coun- te- nance up- on thy ser- vant,

cast ⟨a cheer- ful coun- te- nance up- on thy ser - vant,⟩ cast _____

cast ⟨a

up- on thy ser- vant,

-nance up- on thy ser- vant, up- on thy _____ ser- vant, thy _____ ser- vant, _____

cast ⟨a cheer- ful coun- te-

9. Lord, Remember David

Psalm 132: 1–5

29

nor climb up in- to my bed, in- to my bed;

climb up in- to my bed, nor ⟨climb up in- to my _____

nor climb up _____ in- to my _____ bed, in- to _____ my bed, nor

-to my bed, my _____ bed, nor ⟨climb up _____ in- to my

_ in- to my bed, in- to my bed, nor climb up in-

bed, nor ⟨climb up in- to my bed,⟩ in- to my

34

I will not suf- fer mine eyes to _____ sleep,

bed;⟩ I will not suf- fer mine

climb up in- to my bed; I will not suf- fer mine eyes to _

bed⟩ in- to _ my _____ bed;

-to my _____ bed, in- to my _ bed; I will not suf- fer mine eyes to _____

bed, ⟨in- to my _____ bed;⟩ I

68

God, for the Al- migh- ty God of Ja- cob, for ___

for the Al- migh- ty God,

-on for the Al- migh- ty God, for the Al- migh- ty God

-cob, for ⟨the Al- migh- ty God of ___

-ta- ti- on for the Al- migh- ty God, for the Al- migh- ty

Ja- cob, for ⟨the Al- migh- ty God of Ja-

_ the Al- migh- ty _ God of Ja- cob.

for the Al- migh- ty God of Ja- cob, of ___ Ja- cob.

of Ja- cob, of Ja- cob, of Ja- cob.

Ja- cob,⟩ the ⟨Al- might- ty God of Ja- cob.⟩

God of Ja- - cob, Al- migh- ty God of Ja- cob.

- cob,⟩ for the Al- migh- ty God of ___ Ja- cob.

10. Rejoice in the Lord, O Ye Righteous

Psalm 33:1–4, 21

11. My Song Shall Be Alway

Psalm 89:1–7, 9, 50b

*See the "Critical Notes" for the reconstruction of this anthem.

84

Second part
[Verse]

Medius Decani

Medius Cantoris — *Verse* — O Lord, the ve- ry heav'ns shall praise thy won-der-ous works, _____

Countertenor Decani — *Verse* — O Lord, the ve- ry heav'ns shall praise thy won-der- ous

Countertenor Cantoris — *Verse* — O Lord, the ve- ry

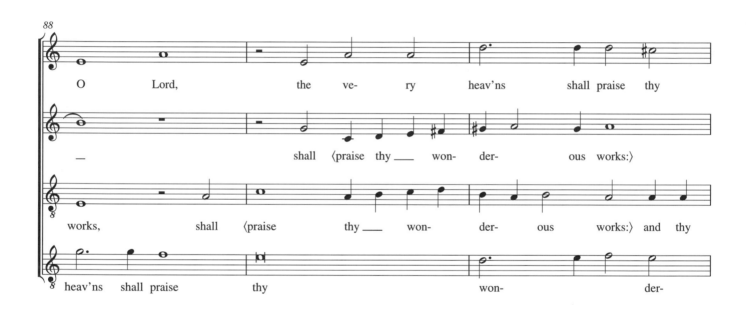

O Lord, the ve- ry heav'ns shall praise thy

— shall ⟨praise thy ___ won- der- ous works:⟩

works, shall ⟨praise thy ___ won- der- ous works:⟩ and thy

heav'ns shall praise thy won- der-

won-der- ous works, thy won- der- ous works: and thy truth in the con- gre-

and thy truth in the con- gre- ga- ti- on _____ of

truth in the con- gre- ga- ti- on of the saints.

-ous works: and thy truth in the con- gre- ga- ti- on of the

Verse Anthem

12. Praise the Lord, the God of Might

A prayer for the King, and the Royal Family.

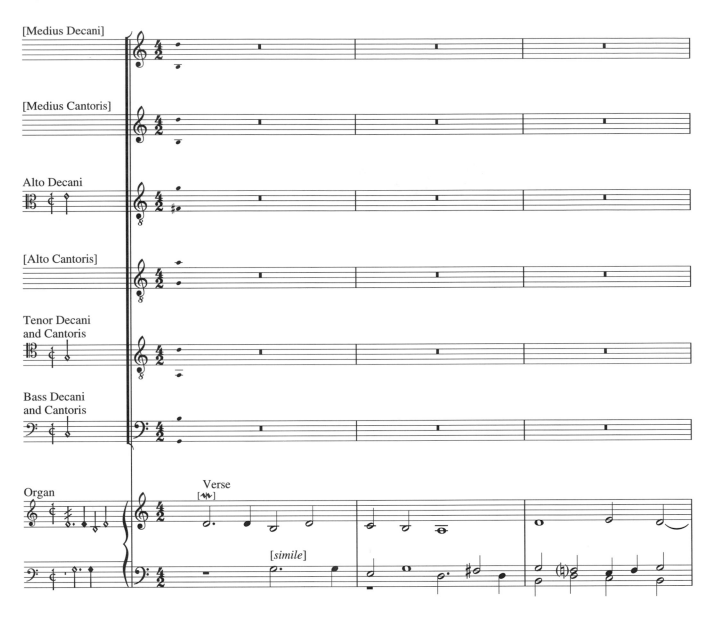

Praise the Lord, the God of might and power

116

Critical Report

Sources and Concordances

None of the surviving manuscripts of Jeffries' music is autograph, nor were any of his works printed during his lifetime. Indeed, all but one of the manuscripts which we have were prepared during his last years or after the presumed date of his death. The page of Sigla and Abbreviations gives, in summary form, all the sources and concordances used in preparing this edition. These were identified primarily from Ralph T. Daniel and Peter Le Huray, *The Sources of English Church Music 1549–1660* (London, 1972), supplemented by the [RISM] *Catalogue of Ascribed Music in Pre-1800 Music Manuscripts Deposited in British Libraries* (London, 1982).

Jeffries' music is found in both secular and liturgical manuscripts, with the secular partbooks being somewhat the earlier in date. It must be remembered that only a very small proportion of the liturgical partbooks in use during the period of 1590–1644 has survived, because of the ravages of time and the destruction wrought to church property during the English Civil War and the Commonwealth which followed. The secular manuscripts may have avoided some of the intentional destruction, but, nevertheless, those that remain are only a small percentage of what once existed. Of the twenty-four separate manuscript sources examined while preparing this edition, three are organ books and two are books of texts. Nine of the remainder are single partbooks and only two are complete sets.

Secular Sources

The earliest surviving source (US-Ws 408) is a single, secular manuscript partbook of ca. 1590, which was acquired by the Folger Shakespeare Library at a Sotheby's sale in February 1939. This treble partbook, it would seem, was originally one of a set of five. Two-thirds of the contents have been identified, and all of these are in five parts, with that in this manuscript being invariably the uppermost. The first 28 pieces are instrumental works, with some transcriptions of motets and madrigals by Orlando di Lasso and Claudio Merulo among the In Nomines and other English pieces. The final seven are unattributed English anthems, setting verses of the psalms. Two of these are ascribed to Jeffries in other sources, while four of the instrumental pieces, including two In Nomines, bear his name. Unfortunately, no other parts for these four pieces are extant. The manuscript has 37 folios of music, each with four staves per side, but with no table or title page. Folios are also missing, the first and last items being incomplete. The pages are oblong, and measure 142 × 193 mm. wide. While "treble" is a satisfactory designation for much of the instrumental music, it is misleading for the voice parts, which have the range of a high mean. This partbook is a source for nos. 6 and 7 and items 2–6 in the appendix.

The other five secular sources date, for their inception, from the middle 1610s. Some of the larger collections would have taken many years to complete. The "Tristitiae Remedium" partbooks (GB-Lbl 29372–77), dated 1616, were compiled by Thomas Myriell, the Rector of St. Stephen Walbrook, London, and contain motets, anthems, and madrigals, totaling more than 220 pieces.[1] The set may not have been completed before 1622, and is the source for nos. 1, 8, and 9.

None of the scribes of the set of Christ Church, Oxford partbooks (Och 56–60) have been identified, nor has its provenance been discovered, although about a quarter of the eighty-odd items of the set can be found in *Tristitiae Remedium*.[2] The bassus is lacking. The set dates from ca. 1615–ca. 1620, although some commentators suggest it may be later. It provides five partbooks for nos. 2 and 3. The survival of both verse parts has been the deciding factor, for choice of source, over Ob Ten 807–11. The set also provides the sole source for no. 5 and concordances for nos. 1 and 9.

All Tenbury manuscripts (originally at Tenbury Wells) are now housed in the Bodleian Library,

Oxford. The set of partbooks Ob Ten 807–11 contains nearly forty pieces—motets, Magnificats, and anthems.[3] One partbook is lacking and the scribe has not been identified. The probable compilation date is ca. 1616–ca. 1618. The set provides the bassus and four concordances for nos. 2 and 3, concordances for no. 1, and the source for items 1 and 7 in the appendix.

The large and important "Drexel" set of manuscripts (US-NYp 4180–85) includes more than 260 items, comprising motets, anthems, madrigals, and instrumental music.[4] The collection was compiled between ca. 1615 and ca. 1630 by John Merro, a lay clerk at Gloucester Cathedral. It is disappointing that this complete set of six partbooks was found to transmit several mistakes, to be very imprecise in underlay, and to omit many more accidentals for no. 10 than the liturgical sources. The set provides concordances for no. 10. Another large collection, also compiled by John Merro, GB-Lbl 17792–96, contains motets, anthems, Services, consort songs, and many instrumental pieces.[5] The sextus is lacking. It would appear that the set was prepared a few years later than the "Drexel" partbooks, with which it shares the same failings. The partbooks provide concordances for no. 10.

Liturgical Sources

Several of the surviving sets of liturgical partbooks date from before the Civil War, in the reign of Charles I, during the period 1625–42.[6] The seven "Barnard" manuscript partbooks, Lcm 1045–51, dated 1625, and containing Services and anthems, are the survivors of an original set of ten.[7] The compilation of this set probably continued for ten or more years to provide material for John Barnard's printed *First Book of Selected Church Musick* of 1641. Although they would not have been used in a liturgical setting, by their contents and format they must be classed as liturgical partbooks. The original tables of Lcm 1049 and 1051 are particularly interesting, in that more than forty full anthems listed there were never transcribed into any of the partbooks. Furthermore, included among these are eight titles of full anthems, naming the composer, which are otherwise unknown. One is "Let my complaints. Jefferies. Trebles," presumably a setting of Psalm 119:169 onward.[8] The "Barnard" partbooks are the only source for no. 11.

The Durham liturgical partbooks dating from before the Civil War are grouped into six sets, three for Services and the remainder largely devoted to anthems.[9] Set 1 consists of DRc C4, C5, C6, C7 second fascicle, C9, and C10, dating from ca. 1630. Set 5 comprises DRc C2, C3, C7 first fascicle, and C14, dating from ca. 1635, although C3 contains nothing by Jeffries. Only two Set 6 anthem books survive, DRc C11

and C16. These are probably slightly later in date than Set 5 but, like Set 5, are copied in the hand of Toby Brookinge (d. 1642). Y 29, the "Dunnington-Jefferson" manuscript, also prepared by Brookinge, was originally a Durham partbook and is closely related to Set 5.[10] Sets 5 and 6 are very precise in notation and underlay, and have been chosen as the sources for no. 10. Set 5 supplies parts for nos. 6 and 7, and Set 1 concordances for no. 10. Y 29 provides a source for no. 7 and a concordance for no. 10. Also from Durham is the organ book DRc A1, dating from ca. 1633–ca. 1638, and largely in the hand of Henry Palmer, a Lay-Clerk of the Cathedral from 1627–40.[11] This manuscript, being marginally preferable to Cp 493, is used as a source for no. 10.

The manuscripts of Peterhouse, Cambridge, deposited in the University Library, are connected to those of Durham through Prebendary John Cosin of Durham, who became Master of Peterhouse in 1634. Having re-modelled the Durham services, Cosin introduced choral services to Peterhouse, bringing there music by Durham composers and manuscripts by Brookinge and other Durham copyists. Four partbooks (Cp 475–78) of the seven comprising the "Former Set" and four (Cp 487, 489–91) of the seven comprising the "Latter Set" of manuscripts contain music by Jeffries, as does the organ book (Cp 493).[12] Cp 489 is a source for no. 10 and the remainder provide concordances.

The "Batten Organ Book" (Ob Ten 791) contains more than 250 anthems and Services, and was compiled ca. 1630–ca. 1635.[13] There has been some dispute whether Adrian Batten was actually the scribe.[14] This manuscript is the source for the organ parts of nos. 1 and 12.

The earliest sections of five partbooks from a probable set of ten (Och 1220–24) were prepared ca. 1640 for use in Christ Church Cathedral, Oxford, possibly by Thomas Tudway, senior.[15] Two of the books (Och 1222–23) contain only the chorus parts of no. 12, as does the single bass partbook from St. John's College (Ojc 180), possibly once used at St. George's Chapel, Windsor.[16] The other three Christ Church manuscripts contain verse and chorus parts and are sources for no. 12.

The remaining liturgical partbooks all date from after the Restoration of the Monarchy in 1660. The manuscript sections of the Gloucester Cathedral partbooks (GL 103 and 105) were prepared by unidentified copyists and are dated ca. 1663. GL 103 is a printed secundus contratenor decani partbook from Barnard's *Selected Church Musick* of 1641, to which fourteen manuscript folios have been added. The page size is 340 × 227 mm. wide, with ten staves per page. GL 105, on the other hand, is a manuscript copy of the tenor cantoris partbook of Barnard's 1641 publication, again with additions. There are 164 pages, the size being 305 × 200 mm. wide, with ten staves per page. The added sections of these books provide sources for no. 4. The Royal College of Music, London, has six of Barnard's printed partbooks, each with manuscript additions.[17] One of these, the bassus cantoris volume (Lcm IA1), contains two pieces in manuscript by Jeffries (nos. 4 and 9). The page size is similar to GL 103, but the hand is quite different from the Gloucester books, and there are only eight staves to the page.

Durham also has partbooks which were prepared after the Restoration.[18] DRc C2* and C15 supply concordances for no. 10, DRc C17 provides concordances for nos. 6, 7, and 10, and DRc C19 is a source for no. 6 and a concordance for nos. 7 and 10. Two further tenor partbooks from Durham, now in the British Library (Lbl 30478 and 30479), dated 1664 and 1670, provide concordances for nos. 6, 7, and 10, and, in the case of Lbl 30479, a source for no. 7.[19] DRc C19 and Lbl 30479 were copied by Alexander Shaw, chorister, sackbutter, and organist at Durham.

Finally, a single bass partbook of ca. 1670 in Christ Church, Oxford (Och 1012) supplies a concordance, and, from the table, the voices employed for no. 7.

Editorial Methods

1. The edition of each anthem, including the presentation of accidentals and underlay, is based strictly on a chosen source. This source is preferably a complete set of partbooks, but, where sets have not survived, are deficient in some respect, or are incomplete, the sources have been assembled from partbooks of different provenances. Where the chosen sources are damaged, obviously in error, unclear, or ambiguous, the editor has fallen back on information from the concordant manuscripts. The aim has been, as far as possible, to give a coherent edition of each piece, based on a prime source. Source information, and, where applicable, discussion about the choice of source partbooks, are given in the critical notes for each anthem.

2. There is no original order to these anthems, nor can one be arrived at by date of composition. Therefore, the order and numbering of the pieces in this edition has been made first by type—consort anthem, full anthem, verse anthem—then by the number of parts in ascending order, and finally by the title in alphabetical order. The vocal and instrumental parts are given in the order highest to lowest, with, for example, "cantus" being placed, if of similar range, above "quintus," and "decani" above "cantoris."

3. The titles given in the partbooks are haphazard and variable. The editor has used the vocal-text incipits given in Daniel and Le Huray, *The Sources of English Church Music 1549–1660* as titles for the anthems.

4. The original clef, key signature, meter signature (if given) and first note are shown for each part on the prefatory staves at the beginning of each anthem. Rests are omitted. It is assumed that accidentals in the original key signatures apply only at the notated pitch. With such a wide variety of sources, the form of the symbols varies considerably, and no attempt has been made to imitate the originals. The symbols used have therefore been standardized. Where there is no data on the prefatory staff the part is lacking in the source and has been reconstructed by the editor. The range of each voice, but not of the instrumental parts in the consort anthems, is given after the modern time signature at the pitch of the modern clef.

5. Where they survive, the source designations of each part are given above the prefatory staves. Where the source has no part name, or where parts have been reconstructed, an editorial designation is given in brackets. The additional designations "decani" and "cantoris," used in the liturgical sources to refer to antiphonal choirs, are added where two parts of the same voice type need to be differentiated. Editorial markings, such as "verse," are enclosed in brackets.

6. Voice parts originally using a C1 clef (C on the bottom line) are transcribed in the treble clef; those originally in a C3, C4, or C5 clef are transcribed in the transposed treble clef, with the bass clef being retained for those with an F4 clef. The justification for using the transposed treble clef for parts originally in a C5 clef is that they are, in fact, of the same range as many of the tenor parts using a C4 clef.

7. Original note lengths are retained, except in the case of final notes, which are sometimes reduced in duration to fit modern measures. Regular barring is added every four minims to the unbarred voice parts, and the measures are numbered throughout each anthem. Corresponding barlines are inserted into the organ parts, which are barred in the sources in an irregular manner, with the measures varying in length from two to twelve minims. The placing of these original barlines is not shown. Single and double barlines in the original voice parts are shown as double barlines.

All the anthems have a ¢ signature and have been transcribed in $\frac{4}{2}$ meter. A $\frac{2}{2}$ measure is occasionally introduced to bring a final or sectional cadence to the beginning of a $\frac{4}{2}$ measure, particularly where one or more parts of the cadence are suspended.

8. A brace is used to connect the organ staves and a bracket connects the voice parts. The eight-part

anthem (no. 11) is treated as a unified contrapuntal whole, the voices dividing for a few measures only into two antiphonal choirs.

9. Mixed "key" signatures occur in two of the pieces, and have been retained in the edition.

10. Ligatures in the source are recorded in the transcription by closed horizontal brackets above the relevant notes. The occasional pairs of quavers are joined with a beam. Most sources have fermatas on final notes, but where these are omitted in some parts, editorial fermatas in brackets are added. In the organ parts, fermatas are placed above each staff.

11. Some partbooks use a succession of minim rests (possibly to assist counting) where rests of larger value might be expected. In the transcription these minim rests have been replaced by rests of larger value. "Long" rests have been subdivided to conform with the regular measures of the transcription.

12. Ties are used to connect notes divided by a bar-line which were one longer note in the source. Conversely, two minims joined by a tie in the original organ part, and occurring within one measure, are given, for the sake of clarity, as a semibreve in the edition. In some of the sources slurs are applied consistently, but in others they are often imprecisely executed and randomly applied. All slurs have been omitted from the edition, but have been taken into account in the placement of the editorial underlay. Editorial ties are indicated by dashed slurs.

13. Organ accompaniments for three of the anthems (nos. 1, 10, and 12) survive in the sources. These organ parts largely give a sufficiently complete accompaniment as they stand, but in all of them there are passages where the texture is much reduced. Editorial additions to these passages are given in small notes and bracketed rests.

14. Directs in the organ parts are of two types: Those which indicate additional notes, often outside the player's reach, and those which duplicate a note on the other staff, usually where a part crosses from one staff to the other. The former are retained in the transcription; the latter are omitted without comment. Where notes of the same pitch and duration occur on different staves, one is omitted without comment.

15. All accidentals placed on the staff, original or in parentheses, are effective, unless countermanded, for the remainder of the measure. Additionally, all original accidentals given in the chosen sources are retained. No naturals are to be found in any of the sources or concordances, where the convention was to cancel a sharp with a flat, and vice-versa. Such sharps and flats are given as naturals in the edition, to conform with modern practice. Accidentals in parentheses are editorial and cautionary, and are used (a) where a previous accidental is countermanded editorially within a mea-

sure; (b) in confirmation of the pitch of a note, where a simultaneous false relation occurs; (c) where an accidental is considered to remain effective in subsequent measures of a part, but is not so marked in the source; (d) where a cautionary accidental is considered helpful to the performers, but only in the part directly affected. Accidentals which are added according to the principles of *musica ficta*, for example to sharpen a leading note or to modify an apparently diminished or augmented interval (melodic or harmonic), or to preserve the imitation between parts, are placed above each note affected. Where a concordance confirms an editorial accidental of any type, this is reported in the critical notes. The same conventions apply to the accidentals in the organ parts except that, since accidentals above the staff are impractical, such *musica ficta* accidentals are shown in brackets. No editorial accidental should be understood as optional, although the editor would be the first to admit that there are some places where a case could be made for a different interpretation.

16. In some of the partbooks, accidentals are sometimes placed one or more notes ahead of the note to which they apparently refer. Such accidentals given in Ob Ten 811 and Ws 408 are placed precisely on the staff at the pitch of the note referred to. Those given in Och 56 and 57 (no. 2, m. 48 and m. 72) are placed ambiguously, but the intention is clear from the context. All these occurrences are reported in the critical notes. In three cases, the accidental aligns with the note preceding that to which it refers. In these cases the report states which note the accidental "precedes and aligns with," and which note it "must refer to."

17. No expression, phrasing, or tempo markings have been added by the editor.

18. Spelling has been modernized, punctuation has been added and standardized, and, where appropriate, capitalization has been introduced. Editorial underlay, resulting from text omissions or from repetition signs in the sources (usually ://:) is enclosed by angle brackets in the edition, with a pair of angle brackets replacing each occurrence of a repetition sign. Editorial additions to the text are placed in square brackets.

19. The number of syllables pronounced in Elizabethan and Jacobean English often differs from modern speech. Apostrophes are introduced into words requiring fewer syllables than in present day usage (ev'n, heav'n, etc.). Conversely, some words had more syllables than now; these are indicated by additional hyphens (won-der-ous, con-gre-ga-ti-on, etc.).

Critical Notes

The critical notes are given in the same order as the anthems of the edition, and are grouped by anthem type. The editorial number and title of each piece are followed by the source information for each anthem, using the abbreviations for voice names given below, the source abbreviations given under "Abbreviations and Sigla," together with the foliation or pagination.

Concordance information lists the other musical sources examined, again using the abbreviations given above. The abbreviations for voice names shown in parentheses give correlation with the part names of the primary source, but are not necessarily the voice names of the concordance.

Text information includes psalm and verses where appropriate, printed or manuscript sources, and omissions from, or variations and additions to, the text which affect the piece as a whole.

The commentary gives information about parts that are lacking, the selection of voice type for reconstructed parts, mixed key signatures, damage to the sources, and the precision or imprecision of the underlay.

The critical notes as a whole report all textual and musical differences between the sources and the edition which are not covered by the principles stated in "Editorial Methods." The locations of the differences within each piece are identified by measure number, voice part name, and note in the measure. An initial tied note is given as note 1. The following abbreviations are employed for part names and durations of notes and rests: C = cantus, M = medius, A = altus, CT = contratenor/countertenor, T = tenor, B = bassus/bass, Q = quintus, Sx = sextus, Org = organ, l = long, br = breve, sbr = semibreve, min = minim, smin = semiminim, q = quaver. Suffixes are added, such as TD = tenor decani, BC = bassus cantoris, CT2 = secundus contratenor. Pitch is defined as follows: C = two octaves below middle C; c = one octave below middle C; c' = middle C; c" = one octave above middle C; b would be a semitone below middle C.

Variants from concordant sources are not normally reported unless they confirm an editorial accidental, or are particularly interesting or revealing.

Consort Anthems

1. If the Lord Himself

Sources. C, Lbl 29372, fols. 143v–144r; Q, Lbl 29376, fols. 130v–131r; A, Lbl 29373, fols. 143v–144r; Sx, Lbl 29377, fols. 25v–26r; T, Lbl 29374, fols. 143v–144r; B, Lbl 29375, fols. 143v–144r; Org, Ob Ten 791, fols. 366r–367r.

Concordances. Och 56–60 (Q, C, T, A, Sx); Ob Ten 807–811 (C, A, Sx, T, B).

Text. Psalm 124:1–7 without the doxology, but including the "Amen." The wording of *BCP* 1592 is

used in verses 5 and 7. This differs from *BCP* by using "which" for "who."

Commentary. Mixed key signatures have been retained, as they occur in all sources except Ob Ten 811, which has a signature of one flat. The editor has taken account of the concordances where the placing of the source underlay is imprecise. Craig Monson, discussing this anthem, argues that, because of errors and omissions in Lbl 29372–77 and Ob Ten 807–811, Och 56–60 is of higher primacy than they, and could have provided their copy text.[20] I would suggest that Lbl 29372–77, which has ligatures where the other sources have none, is part of a separate branch, and that all three sets of partbooks derive from some now-lost archetype. It seems unlikely that a copyist would translate pairs of semibreves into ligatures, especially in instrumental passages. At the end of the organ part (Ob Ten 791) is written "this song hath no name of yᵉ authour."

Notes. M. 16, Q, notes 3–4, placing of "gainst" unclear. Mm. 24–25, A, Ob Ten 808, m. 24 note 3 onward, "at us" set to br d', sbr e♮'. Mm. 42–44, C, m. 42 notes 3–4 underlaid "ev-en," subsequent syllables displaced to the right, Och 57, Ob Ten 807 followed. Mm. 57–58, Q, m. 57 notes 4–5 underlaid "giv-en," subsequent syllables displaced. Mm. 60–61, Q, m. 60 notes 4–5 underlaid "giv-en," subsequent syllables displaced. M. 61, C, note 1 is g'; A, note 3 is ♮, there being no ♭ in the signature at this pitch. M. 62, Org, upper voice, note 4, natural uncertain in source. M. 81, C, note 1 is a dotted min, note 2 omitted, underlay "are de-liv-ered" displaced to the right. M. 86, A, Och 59, Ob Ten 808, note 3 is ♯. M. 94, Sx, Och 60, note 1 is ♮. M. 101, A, note 1 is a min; Sx, note 2, E♭ omitted from signature to end of anthem. M. 105, Sx, Och 809, note 3 is ♮. M. 106, C, Och 57, Ob Ten 807, note 4 is ♯. M. 109, Sx, Och 60, Ob Ten 809, note 4 is ♭.

2. Out of the Deep

Sources. C, Och 56, pp. 146–47; Q, Och 57, pp. 128–29; CT, Och 59, pp. 134–35; T, Och 60, pp. 144–45; Sx, Och 58, pp. 24–25; B, Ob Ten 811, fols. 14v–15r.

Concordance. Ob Ten 807–810 (Q, CT, T, Sx).

Text. Psalm 130:1–7 without the doxology, but with "Amen." The text is as *BCP* except that in v. 6 all sources have "flyeth" as *BCP* 1560, for "fleeth."

Commentary. In the one place where the underlay is unclear, that from the concordance is used.

Notes. M. 2, T, Ob Ten 809, note 1 is ♭. M. 14, Sx, note 3 has "ear." M. 29, Q, notes 2–3 are smins. M.

32, C, note 3 is ♮: Q, notes 1–2 are smins. M. 40, Sx, note 4, ♯ precedes g but must refer to f of m. 41. M. 48, C, note 2, ♯ precedes d' but must refer to c'. M. 56, T, note 3, ♯ precedes and aligns with d' but must refer to c' of m. 57. M. 59, T, note 3 has fermata. M. 63, C, notes 5–6 are smins. M. 72, Q, note 2, ♯ precedes g' but must refer to f'. M. 75, Sx, note 1 is ♯. Mm. 78–79, T, underlay of "demp-ti-on" unclear as slurs imply an extra syllable, Ob Ten 809 followed. M. 82, CT, note 2, ♯ precedes and aligns with e' but must refer to c'.

3. Sing We Merrily

Sources. C, Och 56, pp. 144–45; Q, Och 57, pp. 126–27; CT, Och 59, pp. 132–33; T, Och 60, pp. 142–43; Sx, Och 58, pp. 22–23; B, Ob Ten 811, fols. 13v–14r.

Concordance. Ob Ten 807–810 (Q, CT, T, Sx).

Text. Psalm 81:1–4 as given in *BCP*, but omitting "even in the time appointed," from v. 3, and adding "World without end. Amen." after v. 4.

Commentary. There is some inconsistency in the underlay of "and upon our solemn feast-day" (mm. 39–44). The Ob Ten partbooks have been followed here.

Notes. Mm. 16 and 18, Q, CT, T, Sx, have "shawm" for "psalm." M. 20, B, note 2, ♯ precedes g but must refer to f. M. 23, CT, note 1 has fermata; T, note 4 is a, giving parallel octaves with Q. M. 34, Q, notes 2–3 are a', giving parallel octaves with T. M. 40, Sx, notes 2–4, "our" set to 2 smins, "sol-" to min. M. 42, Q, notes 2–4, "our" set to 2 smins, "sol" to dotted min; CT, note 5, ♭ precedes d' but must refer to e'; Sx, notes 4–6, "our" set to 2 smins, "sol-" to min. M. 43, Sx, Ob Ten 810, note 3 is ♭; B, note 2, ♭ precedes d but must refer to e. M. 44, CT, Sx, note 4 has fermata. M. 54, CT, note 3 has fermata. Mm. 64–65, T, placing of "-out end" unclear, Ob Ten 809 followed.

Full Anthems

4. Praise the Lord, O Ye Servants

Sources. CT, GL 103, fols. 13r–12v; T, GL 105, pp. 120–21; B, Lcm IA1, fols. 39r–38v.

Text. Psalm 113:1–5. Psalm 113 is listed as a Proper Psalm for Evensong on Easter Day in *BCP* 1560. "O" is added to v. 1, and v. 3 is altered in all sources to "The Lord's Name *be* praised." "O praise the Lord, ye people, for evermore. Amen." is added after v. 5.

Commentary. The tenor source establishes the number of parts by the heading "4 voc." There is no evidence that the missing part is a mean; however, in

supplying a replacement part, the editor believes that a medius part best satisfies the problems posed.

Notes. M. 20, B, note 1 is ♮. M. 55, B, notes 5 and 6, placing of text suggests "hea-ven." M. 59, B, note 2 is c.

5. My Love Is Crucified

Source. C, Och 56, pp. 100–101; CT, Och 59, pp. 88–89; Q, Och 57, pp. 82–83; T, Och 60, pp. 98–99.

Text. The author of the poem is not known.

Commentary. This work, perhaps best described as an anthem for domestic use, occurs in the section of the source devoted to five-part pieces. The tenor part is in a later hand than the others. Mixed key signatures have been retained. The bass part, which is lacking in the source, has been supplied by the editor.

Notes. M. 30, C, note 5, placing of "-tal" imprecise, may commence on previous smin. Mm. 48–50, T, m. 48 note 4 onward, editorial text replaces "Christ is my all in all." M. 57, Q, note 1, e is ♮, there being no ♭ in the key signature at this pitch.

6. Praise the Lord, Ye Servants

Sources. [C], Ws 408, fols. 31v, 32r, 33v; CT, DRc C2, pp. 186–88; T, DRc C14, pp. 139–41; B, DRc C19, pp. 95–97.

Concordances. DRc C17 (B); Lbl 30478, 30479 (T).

Text. Psalm 113:1–4. Psalm 113 is listed as a Proper Psalm for Evensong on Easter Day in *BCP* 1560. A final sentence, "O praise the Lord, ye people: from this time forth for evermore. Amen." is added after v. 4.

Commentary. No listing or other indication has been discovered which gives either the number of voices or what they might be. One part is certainly lacking. However, all the identified pieces in Ws 408 are in five parts, and in several sources this anthem is adjacent to Jeffries' "Sing We Merrily," for which the parts are confirmed as MMATB. The editor has therefore supplied the medius part to complete the texture. Two versions of the cantus part are given in Ws 408. Both versions are identical as far as m. 51, note 1. The second version, printed here, accords with the surviving CT, T, and B parts. The first version, given below in example 1, uses similar thematic material, and is two measures longer. There is evidence that fols. 32v and 33r, which contain the first version, were at one time sealed together with pins and sealing wax. The editorial problems are compounded by the number of errors in the sources of the three lower voices, all of which are, unfortunately, repeated in all the concordances. It would appear that errors had crept into the Durham partbooks of the 1630s and were copied faithfully into the later manuscripts.

Example 1. The following cantus part is all that survives of an alternative setting of the last section of "Praise the Lord, Ye Servants" as given in US-Ws MS V.a.408, fols. 32v–33r.

Notes. M. 3, T, note 2 is e; B, note 2 is G. M. 19, C, ♯ precedes min rest but must refer to c". M. 20, B, note 2, placing of "er-" unclear as slur is under notes 3 and 4 only. M. 23, C, note 3, ♯ precedes e" but must refer to c" in m. 24. M. 40, B, note 3 is e. M. 41, B, note 2 is A. Mm. 43–44, C, placing of text infers "hea-vens"; B, clearly "hea-vens." M. 47, B, clearly "hea-vens." M. 49, C, note 4, ♯ precedes a' but must refer to c". M. 51, T, notes 3–6 are given a third lower, f, a, g, f. M. 52, C, note 5, ♯ precedes d" but must refer to c". M. 56, C, note 2, ♯ precedes a' but must refer to c". M. 57, T, note 4, "A-" of "A-men" repeated.

7. SING WE MERRILY

Sources. [C], Ws 408, fols. 29r–30r; CT, DRc C2, pp. 185–86; T, Lbl 30479, fols. 48r–48v; B, Y 29, pp. 39–40.

Concordances. DRc C7 [inc.] (CT); C14 [inc.] (T); C17, C19 (B); Lbl 30478 (T); Och 1012 (B).

Text. Psalm 81:1–4 as given in *BCP*.

Commentary. Although the source partbooks come from widely separated libraries, in fact, apart from Och 1012, all the sources and concordances of the three lower parts originate from Durham Cathedral. The table of Och 1012 establishes the number and type of voice parts by the note "5 p[ar]ts 2 Means." The editor has supplied the missing medius part.

Notes. M. 16, C, note 1, ♯ precedes d" but must refer to c". M. 29, C, note 2, ♭ precedes f' but must refer to b'; B, note 1, Och 1012 has ♭. M. 31, C, note 2, ♭ precedes c" but must refer to e" of m. 32. M. 33, B, note 4, Och 1012 has ♭. M. 37, C, note 2, ♯ precedes b' but must refer to f' of m. 40.

8. IN THEE, O LORD, DO I TRUST

Source. C, Lbl 29372, fol. 142v; Q, Lbl 29376, fol. 129v; A, Lbl 29373, fol. 142v; Sx, Lbl 29377, fol. 24v; T, Lbl 29374, fol. 142v; B, Lbl 29375, fol. 142v.

Text. The verbal text appears to be a paraphrase of Psalm 31:1, 18; while having psalm-like characteristics, it gives the impression that the phrases were contrived to fit existing music. The author of the paraphrase is unknown.

Commentary. The contrived nature of the text, mentioned above, and the unvocal character of the bass part from m. 59 onward, leads the editor to suspect that this piece was conceived as an instrumental fancy. The imprecision of the underlay and the paucity of slurs in the source means that, where the number of notes exceeds the number of syllables, the underlay is effectively editorial. Paradoxically, in those passages marked with a symbol for text repetition, the use of slurs by the copyist often makes his intentions clearer. The notes record those places where the underlay is imprecise.

Notes. Mm. 3–4, Sx, placing of "trust" imprecise. M. 10, Sx, placing of "trust" imprecise. Mm. 10–11, B, placing of "do" imprecise. Mm. 14–15, Q, has "I shall." Mm. 16–17, Sx, has "I shall." M. 33, T, note 1, ♯ below a but must refer to c' of m. 34. Mm. 36–37, B, placing of "my" imprecise. Mm. 40–41, Q, placing of "-vant" imprecise. M. 44, T, placing of "ser-" imprecise. M. 45, T, placing of "ser-" imprecise. M. 61, Sx, placing of "-men" imprecise. Mm. 61–62, Q, placing of "-men" imprecise. Mm. 63–64, A, placing of "-men" imprecise.

9. LORD, REMEMBER DAVID

Source. C, Lbl 29372, fols. 141v–142r; Q, Lbl 29376, fols. 128v–129r; A, Lbl 29373, fols. 141v–142r; Sx, Lbl

29377, fols. 23v–24r; T, Lbl 29374, fols. 141v–142r; B, Lbl 29375, fols. 141v–142r.

Concordances. Lcm IA1 (B); Och 56–60 (C, Q, T, A, Sx).

Text. Psalm 132:1–5 as given in *BCP*. Psalm 132 is one of the Proper Psalms for Evensong on Christmas Day. The source and concordances set "my house" in v. 3, as in *BCP* 1560, whereas *BCP* has "mine house." "Almighty" is set in place of "mighty" in v. 5.

Commentary. This setting presents several editorial problems, particularly with regard to how extensively *musica ficta* should be applied (mm. 17–21). There are several examples of parallel fifths and octaves and a corrupted cadence where poor copying at some earlier stage is suspected (m. 45). Unfortunately, the concordances always agree exactly with the source in these places. The concordances in many cases, however, have clarified the placing of the underlay where the source is imprecise.

Notes. M. 13, A, note 2 is f', Och 59 has e'. M. 18, A, note 5 is c'. Mm. 34–35, Sx, m. 34 note 2, "in-" set to five smins, "to" to min, "my" to min, Och 60 followed; B, underlay as Lcm IA1. M. 43, T, note 2 is a, giving parallel fifths with Sx. M. 44, Sx, note 4 is c', giving parallel octaves with Q. M. 45, T, note 4 is g♯, clashing with Q. M. 50, B, note 2 has "mine." M. 63, T, note 2 is g, giving parallel octaves with Q. M. 72, B, note 2, ♯ precedes and aligns with G but must refer to F.

10. REJOICE IN THE LORD, O YE RIGHTEOUS

Sources. M, Cp 489, fols. 20v–21r; CTD, DRc C2, pp. 183–84; [CTC], DRc C7 (first fascicle), pp. 122–23; TD, DRc C11, pp. 3–4; TC, DRc C14, pp. 136–37; B, DRc C16, pp. 10–11; Org, DRc A1, pp. 275–77.

Concordances. Cp 475–78 (M, CTC, CTD, B); Cp 487 (TD, TC); Cp 490–91 (TC, B); DRc C2* (CTD); DRc C4–6 (CTC, CTC, CTD); DRc C7 (second fascicle) (CTD); DRc C9–10 (TD, TC); DRc C15 (TD); DRc C17 (B); DRc C19 (B); Lbl 17792–96 (M, CTD, CTC, TD, B); Lbl 30478–79 (TC); NYp 4180–85 (M, CTD, TD, B, CTC, TC); Y 29 (B); Cp 493 (Org).

Text. Psalm 33:1–4, 21. The text used is that of *BCP* 1592, which has "sing *psalms* unto him" in v. 2, rather than "sing *praises*" as given in *BCP*. The phrase "World without end. Amen" is added after v. 21. The secular sources NYp 4180–85 and Lbl 17792–96 prefer the word "cheerfully" to the "lustily" of *BCP*.

Commentary. The liturgical sources from Durham and Peterhouse have been preferred, because of their accuracy, to NYp 4180–85, despite the latter being a complete set of partbooks (see "sources"). The "verse" marking (m. 1) in the DRc organ part suggests that the opening four-part passage up to m. 10 was sometimes performed with solo voices. The relevant pages of DRc C11 and C14 have suffered a small amount of damage, details of which are recorded in the notes.

Notes. M. 4, TD, note 2 is a min; Org, lowest voice, note 2 is g. M. 5, M, notes 2–3, placing of "-eth" unclear. M. 18, TD, notes 1–2 are mins. M. 22, CTC, note 1 is a min. M. 30, TD, note 4, "a" lost, hole in paper; Org, upper voice, notes 1–2, additional min e' and min d'. M. 35, TD, note 1, note head lost, hole in paper. Mm. 46–47, CTC, note 1 onward, other MSS have "a" a, "good" b, "cour-" e', "-age" sbr e'. M. 48 note 3 to m. 49 note 1, TD lost, also "of the Lord," corner of page missing. Mm. 49–50, Org, upper staff, lowest voice, beat 3 is br e'. M. 57, Org, lower staff, upper voice, beat 3, sbr a replaced by min rest and min a as Cp 493, lowest voice, note 3, additional min A. M. 58, CTC, note 1 is e'. M. 60, B, note 4 is min. Mm. 70–71, CTC, note 1 onward, other MSS have "our" d, "trust" e, "in" a, b, g♯, a, "thee" e. M. 75, CTC, notes 1–2, duplicates bass at the octave. M. 76, Org, upper staff, note 2, additional direct d'. M. 86, TC, notes 3–4 lost, "men" lost, lower part of page missing.

11. MY SONG SHALL BE ALWAY

Source. MD, Lcm 1045, fol. 131r; MC, Lcm 1048, fols. 114r–115r; CTD, Lcm 1046, fols. 136r–137r; CTC, Lcm 1049, fols. 127v–129r; TD, Lcm 1047, fols. 129v–130v; TC, Lcm 1050, fols. 114r–115r; BC, Lcm 1051, fols. 130v–131v.

Text. Psalm 89:1–7, 9, 50b. Psalm 89 is listed as a Proper Psalm for Evensong on Christmas Day in *BCP* 1560. In v. 5 *BCP* 1560 has "wonderous" in place of *BCP* "wondrous." Verse 6 is modified from "For who" to "And what" by analogy with v. 7.

Commentary. The MD part is lacking up to the last note of m. 117. The preceding folio had been torn out of the partbook before the folios were renumbered, probably in the nineteenth century. The editor has reconstructed the part up to that point. The anthem is described as being in eight parts in all the partbooks except MD and BC. The MC and TC partbooks describe the opening verse section as being in four parts. Three of these remain. As the TC part provides the bass for the four voices, and all the other surviving parts have rests for this section, the missing part must be MD. The number of voices required for the verse section at the beginning of the Second part is not stated. A second bass part is required, in addition to the five surviving verse parts, to supply the real bass in various places, for example, mm. 122–26. The incorrect disposition of parts in the antiphonal passages at mm. 24–29 and mm. 131–34 suggests that the CTD part was written into the CTC partbook by mistake and vice versa. If preferred, these two CT parts may be interchanged. The BD part throughout has been reconstructed by the editor.

Notes. M. 7, CTD, notes 1–2, placing of "Lord" unclear. M. 40, CTD, notes 2–3, placing of "-lish" unclear. Mm. 89–90, CTD, note 5 of m. 89 and note 1 of m. 90, placing of "der-" unclear. M. 93, CTD, note 2 has "thy." M. 95, MC, notes 1 and 3 have "thy." Mm. 100–101, CTC, note 5 of m. 100 and note 1 of m. 101, placing of "clouds" unclear. Mm. 110–11, CTC, note 4 of m. 110 and note 1 of m. 111, placing of "the" unclear. M. 112, CTC, notes 3–4, placing of "the" unclear. Mm. 138–151, all voices, the sources have both "ev'-ry" and "ev-e-ry." M. 154, TD, note 2 is f. Mm. 164–65, TC, note 4 of m. 164 to end of m. 165, a is dotted sbr, d is sbr.

Verse Anthem

12. Praise the Lord, the God of Might

Sources. AD, Och 1220, pp. 259–60; T, Och 1221, pp. 240–41; B, Och 1224, pp. 239–40; Org, Ob Ten 791, fols. 214r–215v; Text, Clifford 1663, pp. 190–91.

Concordances. Och 1222–23 (T, B); Ojc 180 (B); Ob 23, Lbl 6346 (text sources).

Text. The author of the metrical verses is not known. The text is taken from the voice parts and Clifford 1663. Clifford, however, omits the line "The Son, that it redeem'd and saved," and has "with" for "which" in the first line of v. 3. The Och partbooks (and Ob 23) are followed here. Minor variants in the texts are listed in the notes.

Commentary. The surviving partbooks provide texts for AD, TD, TC, BD, and BC voices. Verse passages are given to AD, TD, and BC, while the Och partbooks listed as concordances have chorus parts only. From the surviving voice parts it must be assumed that the missing parts, full and verse, are for medius and alto voices. At m. 87, Ob Ten 791 has the comment "blesse them 6. parts." This might suggest that the other choruses are in five parts, but if so the texture in certain places (mm. 36–37) would be rather bare. The editorial reconstruction has been made, using all the evidence provided by Ob Ten 791 and Clifford 1663, for MMAATB verse and chorus.

Notes. M. 39, AD, note 3 is a br; B, note 2 is a br. M. 74, AD, additional min f' between notes 1 and 2. M.

76, T, note 1 is a sbr. M. 78, T, B, note 2 has "those." M. 80, AD, note 2 has "those." M. 86, no "chorus" indications in voice partbooks, but both T and both B partbooks have musical text. M. 89, Org, lower staff, upper voice, notes 2–3, possible tie. Mm. 97–99, Org, lower staff, upper voice, from m. 97 note 2 to m. 99 note 1, part originally written a third higher, then rewritten at correct pitch. M. 112, B, note 2 has "that." M. 114, B, note 2 has "that." M. 125, Org, upper staff, upper voice, notes 3–4, min g', sbr f♯'. M. 128, T, d in both partbooks.

Critical Notes for Appendix

The principal argument for suggesting that the seven unattributed anthems are by Matthew Jeffries is that they are grouped in sources Ob Ten 807–11 and Ws 408 with anthems positively attributed to him in other sources. The only attributions in these sources are at the end of the final piece of the group, "Out of the deep" in Ob Ten 807, 809, and 811. The group in the Tenbury partbooks are all in the same hand, and, following on directly from one another, were obviously copied in sequence.

In "Behold, How Good and Joyful" and "Let God Arise" there are many examples of themes and scoring similar to other anthems by Jeffries, and both are written in his characteristic "modulatory" style. His liking, after a close on A major, to begin a full passage on F major, are present in both anthems, and his almost obsessional ending "For evermore. Amen" is added to the text of "Let God Arise."

The "modulatory" style can be seen also in the five anthems from Ws 408. Their construction, using short repeated phrases, resembles that of their five-part companion anthems "Praise the Lord, Ye Servants" and "Sing We Merrily."

Consort Anthem

[1] Behold, How Good and Joyful

Sources. M[1], Ob Ten 807, fols. 13v–14r; CT1, Ob Ten 808, fols. 12v–13r; CT2, Ob Ten 809, fols. 13r–13v; T, Ob Ten 810, fols. 11r–11v; B, Ob Ten 811, fols. 11v–12r.

Text. Psalm 133:1–4 as given in *BCP*, with "Amen."

Commentary. The surviving parts, except M1, are marked "6:voc:" It would seem the missing part is a second medius voice.

Notes. Prefatory staff, CT1, the signature of two flats occurs on the initial staff of the source; thereafter there is one flat. The E-flats in mm. 3, 4, and 9 derive from the initial signature.

Full Anthems

[2] BEHOLD NOW, PRAISE THE LORD

Source. [C], Ws 408, fols. 28r–29r.

Text. Psalm 134:1–4 as given in *BCP.*

[3] BOW DOWN THINE EAR

Source. [C], Ws 408, fols. 34r–35r.

Text. Psalm 86:1–5 as given in *BCP.*

Commentary. Verse 3 has a 𝄴 time signature (³⁄₂).

[4] LORD, I AM NOT HIGH-MINDED

Source. [C], Ws 408, fols. 30r–31r.

Text. Psalm 131:1–4 as given in *BCP.*

[5] O SING UNTO THE LORD

Source. [C], Ws 408, fols. 35v–36v.

Text. Psalm 96:1–4 as given in *BCP.* Verse 3 is altered to "and his wonders *to* all people," and "so be it" is added after v. 4.

[6] REJOICE IN THE LORD, O YE RIGHTEOUS

Source. [C], Ws 408, fols. 36v–37v.

Text. Psalm 33:1–?. As with the six-part setting (no. 10), the text used is that of *BCP* 1592, where, in v. 2, "sing psalms" replaces "sing praises."

Commentary. The source is imperfect, breaking off in the second half of v. 4. All the identified works in Ws 408, instrumental and vocal, are in five parts; it can only be assumed that these five anthems are also.

[7] LET GOD ARISE

Source. M [1], Ob Ten 807, fol. 14v; CT1, Ob Ten 808, fols. 13v–14r; CT2, Ob Ten 809, fols. 14r–14v; T, Ob Ten 810, fols. 11v–12v; B, Ob Ten 811, fols. 12r–12v.

Text. Psalm 68:1–3 as given in *BCP.* Psalm 68 is listed as a Proper Psalm for Evensong on Ascension Day in *BCP* 1560, and as one of the set psalms to be used at thanksgiving services on November 5. The phrase "For evermore. Amen." is added after v. 3.

Commentary. Except for the M1 part, the surviving parts of this anthem are marked "6:voc:" It would seem the missing part is a second medius voice.

Notes. M. 7, CT1, note 3 has "thine."

Notes

1. Craig Monson, *Voices and Viols in England 1600–1650: The Sources and the Music* (Ann Arbor, 1982) 17–29, and idem, "Thomas Myriell's Manuscript Collection: One View of Musical Taste in Jacobean London," *Journal of the American Musicological Society* 30 (1977): 419–65. The full title of the set reads "Tristitiae Remedium. Cantiones selectissimae, diversorum tum authorum, tum argumentorum; labore et manu exaratae Thomae Myriell. A.D. 1616."
2. Monson, *Voices and Viols,* 59–69. See also G. E. P. Arkwright, *Catalogue of Music in the Library of Christ Church, Oxford,* Part 1 (London, 1915).
3. Monson, *Voices and Viols,* 70–75. See also Edmund H. Fellowes, *The Catalogue of Manuscripts in the Library of St. Michael's College, Tenbury* (Paris, 1934), 168–69.
4. Monson, *Voices and Viols,* 133–43, 149–53.
5. Monson, *Voices and Viols,* 143–48, 154–57. See also Augustus Hughes-Hughes, *Catalogue of Manuscript Music in the British Museum,* vol. 1 (London, 1906).
6. A discussion and lists of contents of these manuscripts can be found in John Morehen, "The Sources of English Cathedral Music, c. 1617–c. 1644," (Ph.D. dissertation, University of Cambridge, 1969).
7. J. Bunker Clark, "Adrian Batten and John Barnard: Colleagues and Collaborators," *Musica Disciplina* 22 (1968): 216–29. See also Peter Le Huray, "Towards a Definitive Study of Pre-Restoration Anglican Service Music," *Musica Disciplina* 14 (1960): 177–78.
8. The other anthem titles not listed elsewhere are: "Give alms," Thomas Weelkes; "Give sentence with me," Thomas? Boyce; "Godliness is great riches," Edmund Hooper; "Hear my prayer," Hooper; "Let thy merciful ears," Hooper; "Let thy mighty hand," George Marson, 5 parts; and "O praise the Lord," Hooper, [for] trebles.
9. Brian Crosby, *A Catalogue of Durham Cathedral Music Manuscripts* (Oxford, 1986) and idem, "Durham Cathedral's Liturgical Music Manuscripts c. 1620–c. 1640," *Durham University Journal* 35 (1973): 40–51.
10. David Griffiths, *A Catalogue of the Music Manuscripts in York Minster Library* (1981). See also Wyn K. Ford, "An English Liturgical Partbook of the 17th Century," *Journal of the American Musicological Society* 12 (1959): 144–60.
11. Crosby, *Durham Cathedral Music,* 11–12.

12. Dom Anselm Hughes, *Catalogue of the Musical Manuscripts at Peterhouse Cambridge* (Cambridge, 1953). See also Le Huray, "Definitive Study," 180–81.

13. Fellowes, *Tenbury*, 159–63.

14. Le Huray, "Definitive Study," 172–76, and Bunker Clark, "Adrian Batten," 207–18.

15. Le Huray, "Definitive Study," 186. See also Arkwright, *Christ Church*, Part 1.

16. Le Huray, "Definitive Study," 178–79.

17. W. B. Squire and R. Erlebach, "Catalogue of the Manuscripts in the Library of the Royal College of Music," (1931). Typescript in the Royal College of Music Library, the British Library, and Cambridge University Library.

18. Crosby, *Durham Cathedral Music*, 36–45.

19. Hughes-Hughes, *British Museum*, 16–23. See also Ford, "English Liturgical," 144–46, and Crosby, *Durham Cathedral Music*, 245.

20. Monson, *Voices and Viols*, 71–73.

Appendix

Incipits of Unattributed Anthems

[1] Behold, How Good and Joyful

Psalm 133:1–4

[2] Behold Now, Praise the Lord

Psalm 134:1–4

Be- hold _____ now, praise the Lord, ⟨be- hold _____

_ now, praise the Lord:⟩ all ye ser- vants, ⟨all ye ser- vants⟩ of the

[3] Bow Down Thine Ear, O Lord

Psalm 86:1–5

Bow down thine ear, O Lord, bow ⟨down thine ear, O

Lord,⟩ and hear me, and ⟨hear _____ me:⟩ for I am poor,

[4] Lord, I Am Not High-Minded

Psalm 131:1–4

Lord, I am not high- mind- ed, ⟨Lord, I am

not high- mind- ed:⟩ I have no proud looks, ⟨I have no proud

[5] O Sing unto the Lord a New Song

Psalm 96:1–4

O sing un- to the Lord a _____ new song,

O ⟨sing un- to the Lord a new song:⟩ sing un-

[6] Rejoice in the Lord, O Ye Righteous

Psalm 33:1–?

Re- joice in the Lord, O ye righ- te- ous, re- joice ⟨in the

Lord, O ye righ- te- ous:⟩ for it be- com- eth well the just to be

[7] Let God Arise

Psalm 68:1–3

RECENT RESEARCHES IN THE MUSIC OF THE RENAISSANCE
James Haar, general editor